Newspaper Typography

**A Textbook
for Journalism Classes**

Newspaper Typography

A Textbook for Journalism Classes

By

HARTLEY E. JACKSON

Instructor, Division of Industrial Arts Education
San Jose State College
San Jose, California

STANFORD UNIVERSITY PRESS
STANFORD UNIVERSITY, CALIFORNIA

STANFORD   UNIVERSITY   PRESS
STANFORD UNIVERSITY, CALIFORNIA

LONDON: HUMPHREY MILFORD
OXFORD   UNIVERSITY   PRESS
—
THE BAKER AND TAYLOR COMPANY
55 FIFTH AVENUE, NEW YORK
—

Foreword

THIS book is a revision and enlargement of the author's former text, *26 Lead Soldiers,* now in use in many schools and colleges. Teachers who have used the earlier text will find the materials here arranged in a more logical order as well as simplified in detail. New chapters deal with "Newspaper Typography," and "Paper and Ink." Printing presses are given more extended treatment in the chapter on "Presses and Processes."

While the discussions necessarily extend to other forms of printing and typography, it has seemed desirable to focus the chapters sharply upon newspaper typography and the mechanical features of newspaper production.

Grateful acknowledgments are due Dr. Chilton R. Bush, professor and head of the Division of Journalism, Stanford University, and his associates, Assistant Professor Clifford F. Weigle and Mr. Neal E. Van Sooy, and to the several other teachers who have so kindly offered suggestions for the improvement of the text.

HARTLEY E. JACKSON

January 1942

Contents

List of Figures

CHAPTER ONE

Type History and Classification

Gutenberg's invention; sources of type designs; various methods of classifying type faces; need for type knowledge; methods of identifying type faces

TYPE is to the printer what soil is to the farmer—the foundation from which every process starts. Type has an elemental quality. It is primal and fundamental. Printing is the bringing together of type, ink, and paper, in order to transmit thought at a distance in time or space. The ink and the paper are mere tools; type is the essence of printing itself.

Type form persistent.—It is a challenging fact that the physical appearance of type has not changed in the five hundred years that men have printed from movable types. Printing machines have progressed from the first crude wooden press—actually a wine press—to the block-long newspaper presses of today. Illustrations have developed from woodcuts to life-like full-color reproductions. Printing papers have been marvelously improved, and are little like their primitive beginnings. But type is virtually the same now as it was when printing was born—in that glorious hour to which George W. Jones, the great English printer, has applied the quotation: "when the morning stars sang together, and all the sons of God shouted for joy." Few objects in our modern world share this timelessness, this invariable quality.

1

Johann Gutenberg of Mainz, Germany, is called the Father of Printing, because about 1440 the first piece of printing done in Europe with movable types issued from his press. If Gutenberg could see today's types, he undoubtedly would admire their precision and finish; but he would find them otherwise much the same as those he cast for the famous "Forty-two-line Bible."

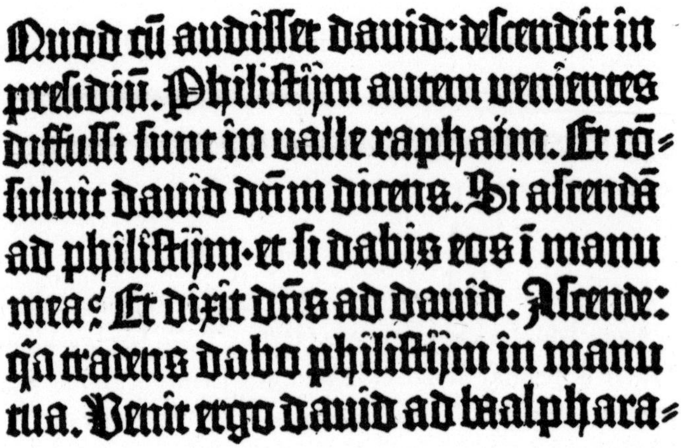
Quod cū audiisset david: descendit in presidiū. Philistiim autem venientes diffusi sunt in valle raphaim. Et cō- suluit david dnm dicens. Si ascendā ad philistiim· et si dabis eos ī manu mea? Et dixit dns ad david. Ascende: q̄a tradens dabo philistiim in manu tua. Venit ergo david ad baalphara-

Fig. 1.—Reproduction of the types used in the great 42-line Bible, which issued from the press of Fust and Schoeffer in Mainz, Germany, about 1451. It is probable that this Black-Letter face was cast from the type molds of Johann Gutenberg. It was about 24-point size.

We know this on account of a slight accident that occurred in printing a fifteenth-century book, the sort of mishap that occurs occasionally even today: A letter pulled up out of the type page when the inking was being done; this letter remained lying on top of the type page when the impression was taken, and printed its own silhouette on the paper. This is how we know what the first types looked like.

Even the cases in which type is kept and the composing "sticks" in which it is set share the ageless quality of type itself. Those used today differ from the earliest ones only in nonessential details.

Designs change slowly.—Type designs repeat the change-less character of the type itself. When one examines the books and other printed matter produced in the last five centuries, he finds only a few basic letter forms. These are modeled on early manuscript letters, which were drawn with brush or reed pen. These designs, with few modifications, are the type faces which are used for most printed matter today.

There have existed fashions in type, like those in dress or ornament. At times certain classes of types have held the center of the stage while others have almost disappeared. There have been numberless attempts to create something new and different; but readers, the court of last decision, invariably have rejected radical changes. Only in the last two decades have original type faces appeared which show promise of surviving.

Four traditional forms.—Since their invention, movable types have grouped themselves according to their characteristics into four distinct classes. These classes are: Black Letter; Script (or Cursive); Gothic (or Sans Serif); and Roman.

In making types the natural tendency was to imitate the best manuscripts of the country where the type had its origin and first use. German manuscript hands were heavy, with angular, flat-end terminals. Gutenberg adopted this model, and his types were what is now called Black Letter. This type also is called German Text, or simply Text. In Germany for centuries books and newspapers have been printed largely in Black Letter types.

Italian scribes wrote their manuscripts in lighter, more grace-ful characters, and in some cases in a sloping, flowing form called Cursive or "running hand." From these models the early printer-typefounders in Italy derived the lighter, more readable Roman types, with graceful bracketed terminals or *serifs,* as they are called. From Cursive writing was developed a sloping Roman form, called, from its origin, Italic. Also from the Cursive hands we have derived the Scripts and modern Cursives.

The earliest use of true Roman types was by Pannartz and

Sweynheym at Subiaco, Italy, about 1464. France adopted this form almost immediately, to the exclusion of the Germanic Black Letter. In England, however, the first printers, William Caxton and his successor Wynkyn de Worde, used Black Letter, and this face was used in English printing to the exclusion of all others until the sixteenth century.

Murice iam croceo matabit uellera tuto.
Sponte fua fandix pafcentef ueftiet agnof.
Ipfe lacte domum referent diftenta capelle.

FIG. 2.—Here is a reproduction of the first Roman letter, modeled upon the written letters of Italian scribes of the period, and cast as type by Sweynheym and Pannartz at Subiaco, Italy, about 1464. It is known as the De Spira type. The specimen is exact size.

The Italic version of Roman types was brought into use by the great Italian scholar-printer, Aldus Manutius. At first only the minuscule form (small or lower-case letters) was made, and early books show a curious effect with Roman capitals combined with Italic lower case. Sloping capitals were introduced early in the sixteenth century.

I n mezzo di duo amanti honefta altera
Vidi una donna, et quel fignor con lei,
Che fra gli huomini regna et fra li Dei;

FIG. 3.—Aldus Manutius, the great Venetian printer of the early sixteenth century, took the cursive hand of Italian scribes as his model for this beautiful Italic type, in which many of his books were printed. Notice that the capitals are Roman; Italic capitals were not cut until later.

Many beautiful Roman *Oldstyle* (or "Old Face") types were designed on the general model. Since printing was done on handmade, wetted papers, with heavy pressure, the thickening of the letters gave a most pleasing effect to early books.

Late in the eighteenth century an English experimenter, John Baskerville, found that he could make paper smooth by pressing it between metal sheets before or after printing. This smooth paper inspired a modification of the design of Roman types. Their contrasts were reduced and their serifs were made more geometrical. Baskerville's letters now are having a renewed vogue. Baskerville and similar faces, such as Scotch Roman, Bulmer, Binny, and Oxford, are called *Transition* types.

At about the time that Baskerville was making smooth paper and redesigning the Roman letter in England, Bodoni, an Italian, and Didot, a Frenchman, also were engaged in modifying this letter form. Their types show evidence of having been drawn with ruler and compasses. The term *Modern* is applied to these formal designs, of which Bodoni is the best present-day example.

The body types used by newspapers are also to be classed as Modern Roman in design. These faces had their origin in the need for simple, strong types for newspaper columns.

Early type classifications.—Most types can be grouped according to the design of certain portions of their individual letters. These details are or have been functional in character. In some cases their original functions pertained to manuscript writing, and were lost sight of when types were cast in metal.

For example, the quill pen used by some of the scribes turned toward the left when held in the hand at a natural angle. If the pen was lifted from the paper at the end of a downward stroke, an awkward and uneven terminal would result. To overcome this the scribe stopped his pen and then pressed downward on it to give a graceful stop to the stroke. These widened ends appear in so-called Oldstyle types today. Such terminals, whatever their design, are called serifs.

While serifs are one of the important features by which types are classified and identified, other details of the various characters should be observed and remembered. Many of these details will be noted in the specimens on pages 15–19.

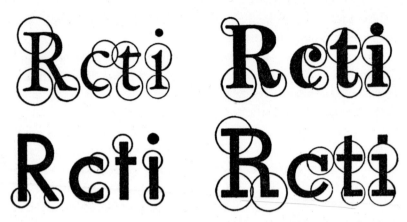

Fig. 4.—Examples of serifs: (left to right) Oldstyle Roman, Modern Roman, Sans Serif, Square Serif.

One distinction between classes is readily made. Roman and Black Letter types have serifs of characteristic forms, while Sans Serifs and Scripts have no serifs.

Black Letter.—*Texts* are based upon manuscript models used in Germany in the Middle Ages. As has been said, this form was the first to be cast in type, and it always has been used for the printing of Germanic languages. A movement began in Germany just before the World War of 1914–1918 to replace the Black Letter, or *Gotischeschrift*, with Roman. After the war,

𝔐𝔢𝔡𝔦𝔢𝔳𝔞𝔩 𝔅𝔬𝔬𝔨𝔰 𝔞𝔯𝔢 𝔞𝔱𝔱𝔯𝔞𝔠𝔱𝔦𝔳𝔢

Fig. 5.—This specimen of Goudy Text, drawn and cut by Fred W. Goudy, the great contemporary American type designer, shows what is probably the best modern example of Black Letter. This is the 30-point size.

the intensified nationalism which fostered the growth of National Socialism in Germany seized upon and glorified for a time all medieval survivals. More recently a change to Roman types again seems to be in prospect.

Two varieties of Black Letter are common in Germanic

printing. They are called Fraktur and Schwabacher. The Fraktur is like Gutenberg's types, and shows the effect of copying brush-made letters. The Schwabacher has pointed serifs, which give a "spiky" effect to the page. Both kinds have been much improved in recent designs and German printing looks much better for the change.

Scripts.—In a strict sense, Scripts are imitations of handwriting. Some manuscript handwriting, however, was more like printed lettering, and derivatives from this kind of hand are better described as *Cursives*.

Spencerian hand set in type

Fig. 6.—The old copy-books displayed examples of what was known as "Spencerian" Script, which was similar to this specimen of 36-point Royal Script. The separate letters are cast in such a way as to appear joined, although close examination will show minute breaks, even when letters are new.

The distinction between Scripts and Cursives is not an easy one to make. Typographers, however, tend to call those in which the separate letters are joined together with continuous lines "Scripts," and the discontinuous forms "Cursives." The typefounders' naming of their faces shows no settled plan in this respect.

Sloping modifications of Roman letters are called *Italics*, and these can be distinguished from Cursives by the fact that Roman characteristics, such as thick and thin strokes and an occasional serif-like terminal, are carried over from the Romans to their Italic counterparts.

There was a time when Texts and Scripts appeared only in "social" printing such as personal cards and wedding announcements. Now, however, in their search for novelty and distinction, typographical designers have adapted both these forms to

the uses of advertising. A number of new Scripts, as well as
older designs, and a few Text faces are now to be found in newspaper and magazine advertising and occasionally in the news
columns of metropolitan papers.

    Sans Serifs.—The general term "Gothic" was used until
recently in this country to describe all square-cut, plain types
without serifs. The same term as used abroad applies, however,
to Black Letter forms. The French words "sans serif"—"without serif"—have now superseded the word Gothic everywhere.

Sans Serif is useful

    Fɪɢ. 7.—Plain, square types like these first came into use in the
Nineteenth Century. The specimen shown, however, is one of the modern, re-designed "Gothics with a college education."

    Gothics were long the printer's standby. Even today Copper-
plate Gothics are to be seen on nine out of ten business cards.
Advertisers of the Victorian era were very partial to faces like
Gothic No. 16 (page 85), and Condensed Gothics (page 85)
were used widely for newspaper headlines until the present decade. Some national advertisers recently turned back to these stiff,
uncompromising types in an effort to impart a certain forthright-
ness to their two-page spreads. However, sales of the old plain
Gothics have declined greatly. Their place has been taken by
new Sans Serif designs which originated in Germany after 1918.

    The change from, say, Gothic No. 18 (page 85) to Tempo
Bold (Fig. 7, above) is a matter of delicate redrawing of shapes
and refining of details. Among the specimens in this book will
be found other examples of what a "college education" has
done to the old square-line forms. These new types express qualities that were entirely foreign to the older letters.

    These enlivened and personalized Sans Serifs have wrought
a whole revolution in design. Sharp angles and blocked masses

of color are the keynotes of this new typography. The oldsters writhe and swear at the blatancy and harshness of many of its examples. In the hands of those who know how to use the Sans Serif form, however, it has served to create many beautiful pieces of printing.

Revival of certain "antique" designs which were popular in the 1880's has raised a problem in type classifications. These are the so-called "Square Serif" types, like Girder, Beton, Stymie, Memphis, and Cairo (page 18).

These designs can be used in combination with or interchanged with the Sans Serifs. Their geometrical character lends itself well to modern functional design. For this reason, and because they "clash" with Romans, the Square Serif letters are usually classed with the Sans Serifs.

The Roman letter.—Roman types, with their associated Italics, constitute the greater portion of whatever we read. They should, therefore, of course, receive major consideration in any discussion of types. The student should be able to distinguish between the two principal classes of Roman, and should be able to identify the commonest species of each at a glance.

To learn to do so he should study many specimens, both single lines and paragraphs. Using the identifying characteristics indicated in the type examples shown in this book, he should attempt to label the various specimens he finds. Then he should have his identifications verified by someone who is adept at this sort of thing. Soon the student will find that Caslon, Garamond, Bodoni, and Cloister will be to him "familiar faces."

One of the first things he must learn is to distinguish between Oldstyle and Modern Romans. In the illustration showing the various serifs (page 6) examples are given of the characteristic letter endings of each of these two classes.

Oldstyle Romans.—Oldstyle derives its charm from the informality of its design. It lacks the strong contrasts of Modern, and is generally felt to be more readable on this account.

It has a warmth and a human feeling that differentiate it sharply from its more austere counterpart. Caslon Old Face (page 16) and Garamond are good examples of Oldstyle faces.

Design first seen *long ago*

FIG. 8.—Recent surveys show that Garamond Oldstyle Roman and Oldstyle Italic, shown above in 36-point size, are today one of the most popular types for advertising use.

Oldstyle serifs are rounded and gracefully curved to meet the strokes. The whole design has a hand-drawn appearance. Curves are fluent and variable. The "swells"—thicker portions of the curves of *o, c,* and so on—are below the centers of the curves.

The slanted tops of letters like *l, b, h, p,* and others, are drawn at a steep angle, yet meet the vertical strokes in a rounded point. Capitals *C* and *S* show at their upper extremity an entirely characteristic modeled form. Lower-case *a* and *r* have a distinguishing "blob," and capital *R* has a "tail" that is unmistakably Oldstyle.

Modern Romans.—The Modern variety of Roman is essentially geometrical in design. Lines are regular and letters symmetrical. Right and left halves and upper and lower portions are alike. The effect is one of dignity and impersonality. Modern Roman faces impart a feeling of strength and firmness. Bodoni (page 15) is extremely regular in design and is frequently cited as the outstanding example of Modern Roman.

Modern serifs are especially mechanical in design. They appear to have been drawn with ruling pen and compasses. They are square and stiff. Vertical strokes meet the serifs at abrupt angles; if a curve is provided to relieve the corner, it is small and mechanical.

The vertical strokes appear to have been constructed with a

straightedge. They are heavier, too, than the horizontal lines. This introduces strong contrasts into the letters. In some ways this thick-and-thin character of Modern Romans is thought to make them less readable. The highly polished papers on which Modern Roman faces usually are printed tend to accentuate their contrasts.

Easily identified *face*

Fɪɢ. 9.—Bodoni is an excellent example of a Modern Roman. The specimen is 36-point Bodoni Bold and Bodoni Bold Italic. Bodoni Regular is of medium weight and Bodoni Book is light.

Nevertheless the plain and straightforward qualities of these letters have made them the preferred ones for many uses. Text-books usually are set in Modern, as are children's books. Newspapers have used Modern body types for more than a century.

Transition types.—So-called Transition faces, used universally in England during the first part of the nineteenth century and preferred by early American printers to all others, disappeared from the typographic scene at about the time that the first Hoe presses were being made in the 'sixties. Only one variety, Scotch Roman, held its place against the Modern Roman deluge of the Victorian era.

Scotch Roman *Italics*

Fɪɢ. 10.—A few types have both Oldstyle and Modern characteristics. The specimen shown is 30-point Scotch Roman, one of these so-called *Transition* types.

At some time between 1900 and 1910 a Transition letter known as Oxford was rescued from oblivion by one or two American printers, and books printed in it were so pleasing to connoisseurs of printing that a mild revival of these prim faces was started. Baskerville is having a tremendous vogue among book printers. Bulmer Roman, with its beautiful Italic, also is widely used.

Engravers' faces.—Besides the types that are used in newspapers and books, there is a whole type-face world devoted to so-called "social" printing. Many Scripts fall in this category, also dozens of specially designed Romans, Gothics, and Texts which have been made for the purpose of the printer of wedding invitations, personal stationery, and certain kinds of business announcements.

Many of these types are imitations of letter designs which have been developed by the copperplate engravers. This is why many of their names carry this suggestion, as Plate Gothic, Engravers' Roman, Tiffany Text, and so on.

Type families.—Discussion of type faces leads to consideration of type families. Any type design is susceptible of many variations. The letters can be compressed or widened; their strokes can be made thicker or thinner or otherwise changed. Throughout these changes will run a certain family resemblance.

For example, there are condensed and extra-condensed Gothics which are used for newspaper headings. These terms are self-explanatory. Some types show three or four degrees of condensation.

Some of the Sans Serifs, on the other hand, are made in different weights—light, medium, demi-bold, bold, extrabold.

The Cheltenham family is one of the largest in multiplicity of variants of its basic design. Below is a list of the principal descendants of Cheltenham Oldstyle. Most of the modifying terms are sufficiently descriptive. A type catalogue will furnish specimens.

Not all types have so many variants, but Cheltenham is a good example of what a typefounder can do with a family when the demand arises.

Cheltenham Oldstyle and Italic
Cheltenham Medium and Italic
Cheltenham Oldstyle Condensed
Cheltenham Medium Expanded
Cheltenham Medium Condensed
Cheltenham Wide
Cheltenham Bold and Bold Italic
Cheltenham Bold Condensed and Bold Condensed Italic
Cheltenham Bold Extended
Cheltenham Extra Bold
Cheltenham Extra Bold Condensed
Cheltenham Extra Bold Condensed Title
Cheltenham Bold Outline
Cheltenham Inline
Cheltenham Inline Extra Condensed
Cheltenham Inline Extended

Classification by use suggested.—Gilbert Farrar, typographic counsel, has suggested the possibility of classifying types according to use. He offers six such classes: neutral, formal, informal, block, rugged, and occasional.

In the *neutral* group he places Caslon Oldstyle. The assumption is that this face can be used for almost any purpose.

Formal types, like Bodoni, Baskerville, and Century, are contrasted with *informal* ones, like Garamond and Cloister. Formal types serve the uses of such people as bankers, professional men, and textbook publishers. Informal types are for cosmeticians, women's wear shops, and so on.

Block types include Sans Serifs and the Square Serif group. Uses here are subordinate to method of use. Many trades can use them, Farrar says, if they are wisely handled.

Rugged types, like Cooper Black (page 19), are supposed to be good for grocers' advertising and for the tabloids' thunderings.

Occasional types are to be used sparingly to lighten the monotony of more formal ones. Here Mr. Farrar places the new advertising Scripts, and oddities like Lydian (page 19).

To identify type faces.—Given a type specimen to identify, one may proceed as follows:

There are four general groups or classes of types: Romans, which are in turn subdivided into Oldstyle, Modern, and Transition styles; Sans Serifs, which include Square Serifs; Scripts (usually connected forms) and Cursives; and Texts, or Black Letter styles.

Having decided upon the general class into which the type under consideration may fall, the next step is to compare it with identified specimens of types of that class.

Some of the following letters in most type faces have strong "personal" features, useful in identification:

A C E G L M R S T

a c e f g i l r s t y

To compare individual letters on two pages of print, one specimen should be folded and placed beside the other in such a way as to bring identical letters side by side. This is a good way to compare sizes of types also.

Sometimes a majority of the letters in a specimen correspond to some face in a type catalogue but one or two letters of the alphabet are quite different. This comes from the care exercised by different typefounders and matrix makers to avoid copying designs of others too closely. (The patent rights to a type face may be ignored safely by changing a few letters or their details.) If most of the letters agree, identification may be concluded.

The Sans Serifs of different makers often are difficult to distinguish from each other. Generally it will be enough to say "similar to Metroblack," or "like Memphis."

Bodoni Family 1 2 CAPS

This distinctive type face of sharp contrast has been developed from the designs of Giambattista Bodoni, a seventeenth-century Italian. A large family of related faces have been modeled on the basic letter forms. All Bodoni types are distinguished by their thick-and-thin strokes and by the geometrical character of their outlines and elements. [*Set in Bodoni Book with Italic.*]

A C E G L M R S T

Bodoni serifs are straight, thin lines; the heavy strokes of the capitals narrow down abruptly to join the thin strokes; the *R* ends in a short up-turn.

a c e f g i l r s t y

Here again the thick-and-thin strokes merge abruptly, and serifs are thin, straight lines; descending strokes of *g*, *j*, *p*, and *q* are long; the *t* is short.

Expression: Extreme formality and dignity; purity; height; rhythmic ideas; coldness; exclusiveness.

Newspaper uses: Advertisers use more Bodoni than any other letter; headlines are set in traditional styles and especially in flush-left forms, using all-caps or caps and lower case lines of all the members of this large family.

Bodoni Bold 1 2 CAPS

This member of the Bodoni family is most often seen in headlines.

Bodoni Bold Italic 1 2 CAPS

The Bold Italic of Bodoni is frequently seen in box headings.

Bodoni Bold Condensed 1 2 CAPS

This condensed form of the basic Bodoni design is widely used for newspaper headlines, usually set in traditional forms and in caps.

Ultra Bodoni 1 2 CAPS

Here is the extreme in thick-and-thin. Ultra Bodoni is bold enough to please the exclamatory advertiser, yet it is dignified and readable.

Caslon Oldstyle 1 2 CAPS

William Caslon designed this type face about 1720 and it has fathered a large family. Caslon Bold and Bold Condensed have seen use as newspaper headline faces. Caslon prints well on unsurfaced papers; and tests have shown that this is one of the most readable of type designs. [*Caslon Oldstyle with Italic.*]

A C E G L M R S T

Note the curved end stroke at the top of the *A*; the distinctive sharp-pointed serifs; the unusual conformations which end the *C, R, S*; and the strong "color"

a c e f g i l r s t y

Here again one sees the distinctive Caslon terminals, particularly on the *c, g,* and *s*. Note the sloping tops of the *i, l,* and *r*, and the short *t*.

Expression: Informality; freedom; friendliness; craftsmanship; sturdiness; grace; security; spaciousness.

Newspaper uses: As body type for distinctive advertisements; for advertising display and headlines, Bold, Bold Italic, Bold Condensed.

Cloister Bold   1   2   CAPS

This design dates back to 1489, when Nicolas Jensen first used a similar type face. Cloister is slightly heavier in mass than Caslon, although its letter strokes are more uniform throughout. While Cloister is essentially a type for unsurfaced papers, it can be used effectively on coated papers. Boldface versions are used for headlines.

A C E G L M R S T

These serifs are thick and slightly concave on their lower sides; the club-shaped terminals of the *C* and *S* are distinctive; the top serifs of the *M* extend both ways.

a c e f g i l r s t y

The "tails" of *y* and *g* are noticeable; the slanting stroke of the *e* extends beyond the curve; the lower serif on the *r* projects to the right.

Expression: Great dignity and formality; permanence; warmth; hospitality; frankness; richness.

Newspaper uses: As body type in agency electros; Cloister Bold Condensed is widely used for headlines, usually in caps.

Century Expanded 1 2 CAPS

Plain types for plain purposes is the slogan of this and other types that bear the name *Century*. Century Expanded long was favored as a newspaper body type, and many textbooks are set in this or similar faces. Century *Oldstyle* bears a strong family resemblance to the Expanded, which is a *Modern* Roman design.

A C E G L M R S T

The flat-topped *T* with sloping ends is characteristic of all Century types; these ends appear also on *E* and *F;* the cleft *G* and curly-tailed *R* also are notable.

a c e f g i l r s t y

Round dots end the upper strokes of *a, f, g, c,* and *r,* and bottom stroke of *y; p* and *d* (top line) are deeply cleft; all lower-case letters are large in proportion to caps.

Expression: "Horse-and-Buggy" days; plainness; sturdiness; direct-ness; comfort; common things.

Newspaper uses: Century is seen occasionally in the editorial col-umns; Century Bold Condensed and Bold Italic are headline types.

Cheltenham Oldstyle 1 2 CAPS

This twentieth-century design captured first place in newspaper offices between 1910 and 1920, only to be displaced by Bodoni and the new Sans Serifs in the years that followed. The simplicity and dignity of the Cheltenham design must be recognized, although it lacks the individ-uality of the classical Oldstyle Romans. The Italic is pleasing.

A C E G L M R S T

The Cheltenham serif is unmistakable. It blends into the letter strokes with a smooth curve, has slightly tapered, flat ends, and has a horizontal bottom or top.

a c e f g i l r s t y

Lower-case *f, g, s,* and *r* are the most readily identifiable of the Cheltenham letters. The close fitting of individual letters of words is also noticeable.

Expression: Through constant use Cheltenham has come to connote a certain earthiness and directness.

Newspaper uses: Cheltenham Bold for display and for headlines; Cheltenham Light for editorials and features.

Sans Serif Types 1 2 CAPS

Nearly all the graceful Sans Serif forms now widely used are variants of a basic form known as Futura. Slight modifications occur in the types offered by various makers, but the distinctive features of the design are recognizable, even in sloping and condensed forms.

A C E G H M R S T

The low bar of the *A* is contrasted to the high center stroke of *E* and *H*; the sides of *M* slope inward; *R* has a straight "tail."

a c e f g i l r s t y

The design of lower-case *a* and *t* are notable characteristics; *c* (and also *C*) end as though they had been cut off at a vertical line.

Expression: Simplicity; structure; modernity; indestructibility; integrity; peace; precision.

Newspaper uses: Advertisements set entirely in Sans Serifs, or with Sans Serif main display lines, are seen side by side with Sans Serifs.

Square Serifs 1 2 CAPS

These types are easily recognized by their plain, uniform strokes, which not only make the letters but also form the heavy, rectangular serifs. The members of families of this design range from thin-line forms through graded series up to the heaviest of all faces.

A C E G L M R S T

All capitals have full serifs, and the *A* has a double top; terminal strokes of the *S* are vertical; the *O* and *G* are circular in normal designs.

a c e f g i l r s t y

Two forms are available for several letters, notably *a, f, r,* and *y*; all, however, have the distinctive square serifs and uniform strokes.

Expression: Mechanistic; architectural; exactness; strength; permanence; simplicity; truth.

Newspaper uses: A few newspapers use the square serifs, both normal and condensed in medium bold weights, for streamlined headlines.

Cooper Black   1   2   CAPS

To meet the demand for bigger and blacker types, Oswald Cooper designed this face.

Lydian with *its Italic* 1 2 CAPS

This family also includes Lydian Bold with Italic, and Lydian Cursive.

Conclusion.—In concluding this chapter on the classes and kinds of type the student may feel that the subject is so intricate that it is hopeless for him to attempt to cope with it. To him it should be said that the best anyone can do is to make a beginning. A few of the commoner faces should be studied and these types identified wherever found.

The student should add to his type knowledge whenever possible. When he gets a job with a newspaper he should secure its headline schedule immediately and learn the names of its types.

Type-foundry specimen books and machine-matrix catalogues sometimes may be had for the asking; otherwise they may be purchased like other books. Leaflets showing individual faces in their various sizes and associations are circulated abundantly by all manufacturers and may be had on request.

The student should start a file of type information of every nature and should endeavor to keep abreast of the most recent designs. Here the trade papers, both those concerned with journalism and those which deal with advertising and printing, are invaluable. These papers usually are available in newspaper offices or at the public libraries.

CHAPTER TWO

Physical Characteristics of Type

Composition and characteristics of type metal;
parts of the type letter; how type is made; how type
is fonted and sold

Physical qualities of type.—Upon examining a piece of type one readily observes some of its physical characteristics. In color and heaviness the material resembles lead, which constitutes the largest part of the alloy. In hardness the metal approaches tin, which is another of its constituents. Scratched with a sharp point, it cuts easily and shows a bright, silvery surface; this soon tarnishes in the air, however, to the lead-gray of the original surface.

Type will stand much handling. It seldom is injured in the ordinary course of being set up, printed from, and replaced in the case. Foundry type, if not abused, will give hundreds of thousands of clear impressions before it wears out. But any type can be damaged irreparably by careless handling which bruises or scratches the printing surface.

Constitution of type metal.—Some of the qualities of type, such as its hardness and smoothness, vary according to its composition. Its melting point and its characteristics when melted also depend upon its constituents. Alloys used for foundry, or hand type, are different from those used in typesetting machines. Hand type usually is harder and more dense. Small letters, moreover, are made of a more compact alloy than large letters.

The principal metals used in type alloys are lead, tin, and antimony. Tin comprises from 2 to 6 per cent of the mixture, and antimony from 8 to 12 per cent. Lead makes up the remainder. Sometimes small quantities of other metals are added. The American Type Founders Company adds a small amount of copper to its types in order to make them harder.

A large manufacturer of type metals explains the purpose of each constituent of the alloy as follows:

> In understanding how the eutectic [lowest melting] point is achieved, it must first be borne in mind that lead by itself has a melting point of 621 degrees Fahrenheit and antimony a melting point of 1,166 degrees.
>
> Yet the addition of one per cent of antimony to lead produces a reduction of the melting point, and increasing additions bring it down to the proper melting point of type metal, 475 degrees.
>
> This is reached by the addition of 12 per cent of antimony. Further additions of antimony raise the melting point, instead of lowering it.
>
> Antimony not only lowers the melting point of the alloy but improves its fluidity. Its further contribution is that of causing the alloy to expand at the moment of solidification, so that it fills the mold sharply. But the expansion is only momentary and is followed by immediate contraction, as it cools. The expansion is responsible for sharp impression. The subsequent contraction permits the cast to be readily ejected from its matrix. Addition of the third element, tin, neither increases nor lowers the melting point. Its contribution to the working quality of the alloy is highly valuable, including its function of imparting a smoother type face, that takes ink much better.

Repeated use of metal in the melting pots of typesetting machines results both in oxidation, principally of the tin, and in separation of this element from the alloy. It becomes necessary from time to time to re-smelt the metal and replace loss.

The type mold.—Foundry type is cast in an adjustable mold which is essentially a steel cell closed at one end by the matrix and open at the other to receive the molten metal. The letters are cast one at a time by automatic machines, the process differing little from the handcasting of the earliest founders.

Matrices.—Matrices are made of brass. A steel punch which bears the form of the letter is impressed in a prepared brass blank. Composing-machine "mats" take special forms in order to function in the assembling and distributing processes of the machines; but otherwise they are like those used for foundry types.

The punches which form the matrices are made of very hard steel. Punches formerly were made by hand. The work of forming the letters in the steel was slow and laborious, and required a skill that came only with years of training. These steel punches tend to break under pressure. For this reason, only a few matrices can be "struck" from a punch. It is stated that the invention of the punch-cutting machine, by Lynn Benton in 1884, made possible the introduction of the Linotype and, inferentially, all other composing machines. Without Benton's device it would take an army of highly skilled men to make the tremendous number of punches which are needed for the millions of matrices these machines use. Benton's machine operates rapidly and accurately and makes either the punch, or the matrices directly.

What "type-high" means.—At first glance the student may estimate the height of type to be an inch. It would seem logical that a usual unit of measurement would be applied to a product as universally used as type is. But this is not the case. The height of type in the United States and England is nine hundred and eighteen thousandths of an inch (0.918 in.). This measure is called *type-high*. *Height to paper* means the same thing.

German and French types exceed ours in height. Many imported types show evidence of having been cut down to the American standard.

The nick.—A prominent feature of all type is the *nick* or *nicks*. These small grooves in the body of the type are important to the compositor in several ways. By means of them he can place letters correctly in his stick without looking at their faces. The sizes or positions of the nicks also help him to differentiate between types which resemble each other closely. Moreover, certain small types used in commercial printing are made in a series of closely graduated sizes, and it is the custom to distinguish the sizes by the number of the nicks. When the compositor is *distributing* such types—putting them back in their places after use—these nicks help him to prevent mistakes.

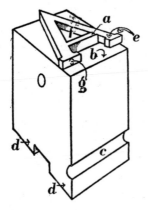

Fig. 11.—Drawing of a type character to show (*a*) face; (*b*) shoulder; (*c*) nick; (*d*) feet; (*e*) serifs; (*f*) void; (*g*) drive.

Most types have their nicks near the foot of the body on the side toward the bottom of the letter. Some French types, however, are nicked on the opposite side and toward the head or top of the letter.

The type face.—At the upper end of a letter is its printing surface, or, as it is called more simply, the *face*. The face is raised a measurable distance above the surrounding surface. Centers of such letters as *o* and *a*, and other "voids," must be deep enough to prevent ink from filling them and marring the print.

Most letters are set back a little from the edge of the type body, but some others, notably *f*'s and Italic capitals, overhang the body. These overhanging portions of the letter are called *kerns*. Types with kerned letters are not suitable for newspaper purposes, since the projections break off unless handled very carefully.

In most types, between the lower edge of the capitals and the edge of the body there is a comparatively wide blank area. This is called the *shoulder*. It provides the room necessary for the "tails" of descending letters such as *g, j, p, q,* and *y*. In some types these *descenders* are quite long. The effect of this wide shoulder is to increase the spacing between lines. The student will find that two types having the same *body* size may vary widely in *letter* size, depending upon the alignment and the length of the ascenders and the descenders.

Alignment.—The word *line* has a special significance to the printer. It is an abbreviation for *alignment*. This term is well understood by those who use a typewriter. Letters are expected to align, according to their conformation, with an imaginary horizontal line drawn at the base of the capitals. Lack of this alignment is a blemish in both typewriting and printing.

Fig. 12.—Alignments: (left to right) standard line; original line; script line; title line.

For many years each type face had its own alignment at the whim of the designer. If one wished to set two kinds of type in the same line, it was necessary to align them with thin strips of metal or paper above and below the letters. American typefounders, with few exceptions, have adjusted their matrices so that now there are only four principal alignments. These take care of all the various conditions that arise.

Most common types are on *standard line*. This allows approximately one-sixth of the body for shoulder.

If the descending strokes of the letters *g, j, p, q,* and *y* are longer than can be accommodated on standard line, *script* (or *art*) *line* is used. This is also used for the types called *Scripts*— imitations of handwriting.

The alignment of Caslon Old Face is intermediate between the two just mentioned. This ancient face, first cut in 1720, retains its *original line*, which is used also for some other faces.

When fonts consist of capitals only and no lower case is contemplated, it is not necessary to allow for descending letters. Thus the shoulder can be eliminated and the type face cast almost to cover the body. This alignment is called *title line*. This word "title" is used in names of types to indicate all-cap fonts cast without shoulders. Many heading types are cast on title line.

Differences in alignment cause great variation in the apparent sizes of type which otherwise are cast on the same body and bear the same point-size designation. This will be seen by comparing the specimens of book types in a type-foundry catalogue.

Other type features.—The height of the letter proper from the shoulder to the face is spoken of as the *drive*. This part of the type is made in the matrix, while the rest is made in the mold. In various countries, and with different founders in the same country, the depth of drive varies. Some French types are notable for their deep drive, and all English Linotype matrices are deeper than those made in the United States. This means that the molds are not the same in height and that Linotype matrices cannot be used interchangeably by these countries.

A type letter must rest firmly and perpendicularly upon its base. For this reason it is provided with *feet*—two parallel flat surfaces, separated by a narrow groove. When type is carelessly handled or is loosely spaced in setting, it often leans to one side or the other. In this case it is said to be "off its feet."

When type is off its feet, only a portion of the printing surface meets the paper and the letters appear imperfect in the proof.

The height of the type body gives the *point size*. The width of the type body varies according to the individual letters, and is called the *set*, or *set width*. These terms will be explained in more detail in the next chapter.

How type is sold; the font.—After final inspection, the letters of each size are set in alphabetical order in lines, and wrapped in one or more packages. A collection of all the characters required for a given purpose is called a *font*, or in older times a "fount." The proportionate number of each character has been worked out for each weight and kind of font. *Cap fonts* are composed entirely of capitals with points and figures. *Lower-case fonts* are made up of the small letters. *Small capitals*, which are made for many faces, are fonted separately.

Typefounders list *job fonts* and *weight fonts*. The former are stated in some catalogues to contain a specified number of *a*'s— so many capital *A*'s, or so many lower-case *a*'s, or so many small capital *A*'s, as the case may be. Ordinarily one lower-case font and one cap font combined contain enough letters for a minimum case, which may serve the needs of a small commercial shop. Most printers purchase type in weight-font quantities. Weight fonts are sold by the pound. Font schemes are planned for average needs. Theoretically, with ordinary "copy," the compositor who sets text matter in his own language until his case is empty runs out of all letters of the alphabet at once.

Costs of foundry type.—The metal in a letter costs much less than it costs to make the letter. For this reason, small sizes of type cost more per pound than large. If we compare the prices of single letters, however, large types cost a great deal more than small.

For example, a job font of 6-point Bodoni Bold contains 25 capital *A*'s and 49 lower-case *a*'s, and costs approximately $2.00. A job font of 72-point Bodoni Bold containing only three *A*'s and four *a*'s costs approximately $12.60. Intermediate sizes range between these two.

A *California case* will hold as much as 40 or 45 pounds of type; but in most instances cases are not filled. In general the average case in a typical print shop, with the type it contains, represents an investment of $10.

A type *series,* consisting of all the common sizes of a type face with its accompanying Italic, and in quantities sufficiently large to be practical, requires at least twenty-five cases and costs from $250 up.

In a later chapter the costs of machine equipment will be discussed, together with the comparative costs of hand composition and machine composition.

CHAPTER THREE

Printers' Measurements

The point system; type sizes; pica ems and other ems; agate lines; copy-fitting methods with four typical problems

THE system by which type is measured may seem difficult at first to the beginner. Really it is quite simple. There are two elements of the type body that must be stated accurately. For this purpose two terms are used. These are *point size* and *set em*. They are understood readily as the latitude and longitude of type when it is set in lines—its "up-and-down" and its "right-and-left." The height of a line of type is measured in *points*, and its width in *ems*.

Formerly the many different sizes of type bore names. These names still are heard occasionally in printing offices. Three of them are commonly used as synonyms for the point sizes which they formerly described. The small type used for classified advertising, for example, usually is called *agate;* its other name is 5½-point. Similarly, *nonpareil* and *pica* are heard frequently instead of 6-point and 12-point, respectively. Lack of a basic unit of size occasioned much confusion in the making of type. The *brevier* size of one typefounder, for example, might be larger or smaller than the brevier of another; two such fonts could not be set together, nor could they make use of the same spacing materials.

28

The point system.—Attempts to remedy this state of affairs started as early as the eighteenth century. In 1737 a French printer named Fournier planned a system of uniform type sizes. He divided the inch of his day into 72 parts, or *points*. Each size of type was a multiple of this small unit. Fournier's system was adopted as law, thus governing all typefounders in France.

In 1770 Didot, another French printer, modified the Fournier point to conform with the (then) French inch. This meant increasing the earlier unit to 0.0148 inch, which is the standard Didot point used in France today. It is slightly larger than our point.

It was not until 1887 that a Californian, Nelson W. Hawks, succeeded in persuading the typefounders of the United States to adopt a standard unit. This is the *American point,* and it measures 0.01384 inch.

The American point system, as it is called, is applied to everything the printer uses. Not only his types but also his spacing materials and all his tools and gauges conform to this unit.

Because of its universal use, it is unfortunate that the point is not an exact multiple of the inch. Seventy-two points make 0.99648 inch. The difference between this and a full inch is less than the thickness of a thin piece of writing paper. For most purposes it is sufficiently accurate to say that 72 points make an inch. But on long measurements, such as the length of a newspaper page, the error multiplies itself into an appreciable fraction of an inch.

Various units.—The *set em,* or more simply, the *em,* is a linear measure derived from the type body used. *The em of any size type is the square of its body.*

Line lengths are expressed as the number of ems of a given size that make up the stated length. A standard newspaper column, for example, has a width of twelve 12-point ems or twenty-four 6-point ems or eighteen 8-point ems. The column is 144 points wide, and it can be also so specified.

It should be clear that there are as many kinds of ems as there are sizes of types; also that a line set in small type will contain more ems than one set in large.

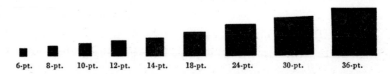

6-pt.   8-pt.   10-pt.   12-pt.   14-pt.   18-pt.   24-pt.   30-pt.   36-pt.

Fig. 13.—Comparative sizes of the square ems of various type sizes

Another measure that is sometimes used is the *en.* This is half an em. Two ens make an em. The similarity of these two is confusing when they are spoken. For this reason the printer often says "mut" or "mutton" for *em,* and "nut" for *en.*

The number of ems set by a composing-machine operator during a working "shift" is called his "string." Type still is set "by the piece" in some localities, and payment to the operator is based upon the number of ems set. Prices for "trade" composition—that is, for composition produced by a specialist for a printer—often are specified by the thousand ems.

The pica em.—There is only one em size that has special importance to the general student. This is the 12-point or *pica em.* It is generally called just "a pica." This unit is almost exactly one-sixth of an inch. While it is specifically the name of a *square* type unit, it is applied universally as a unit of *length.*

All blanking-out materials are made, and printers' tools such as composing sticks and machine gauges are graduated, in multiples of the pica or half-pica. This means that nearly every line of type, either hand- or machine-set, and of any size, will be an integral number of picas in width.

Irregular measures are expressed as a certain number of picas plus a number of points. Such measures are avoided wherever possible as impracticable and confusing. The printer has an expressive term for all irregular sizes or lengths; he calls them "bastard."

Picas and points.—In specifying type for any purpose, we state the *height* of the line of letters in *points* and its *width* in *picas*.

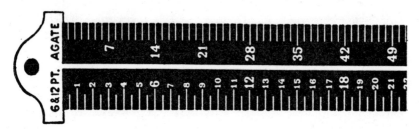

FIG. 14.—Section of printer's line gauge. Full length is usually 72 picas.

Table of measurements.—In summing up printers' measurements, it is customary, and in most cases quite sufficient, to neglect the small inequalities and to say that

72 points equal 1 inch
12 points equal 1 pica (this is exact)
 6 picas equal 1 inch
72 picas equal 1 foot

The agate line.—This is another unit of type measurement that must be known to the student, particularly if he studies advertising. Fourteen agate lines make one inch.

Agate type theoretically is $5\frac{1}{2}$-point. Fourteen lines of $5\frac{1}{2}$-point type would measure just a little over one inch in depth. It is the practice to make $5\frac{1}{2}$-point type slightly smaller so that 14 agate lines exactly equal an inch.

Agate lines may be calculated from the number of column inches, by multiplying by 14.

Classified advertising, sold by the line, usually is set in

agate type. Display advertising rates also are quoted by a large number of newspapers at so much per agate line. In newspaper rate cards, particularly those for "national" advertising, the agate line has largely displaced the older column-inch measurement. Legal advertising in most cases is sold by the line, and often by the agate line. Some states, however, specify the "square" as the basis for charges for legal advertising. This unit is not the same in all states and is open to criticism for this reason.

Agate-line measurement is used universally to state newspaper advertising volume. The term *total linage* is a measure of the number of agate lines of advertising carried by a newspaper for a period stated. This makes it possible to compare various newspapers with respect to advertising volume.

Size of newspapers.—Page size of newspapers is stated almost always in number of columns wide by number of inches deep. If the over-all width is to be given, it may be expressed in picas. For example, a newspaper page with eight 12-pica columns separated with half-pica column rules will measure $99\frac{1}{2}$ picas wide. This is 16.525 (slightly over $16\frac{1}{2}$) inches.

In length the type page commonly is described in inches, since retail advertising space frequently is sold on the column-inch basis. It should be noted that there is a wide variation in the type-page length of various newspapers in the United States. This length, for standard, full-size papers, varies from 20 to 22 inches. Tabloid, half-size pages are 16 to 18 inches long—type measurement.

Two common units.—When type for newspapers formerly was set by hand in a composing stick, a *stickful* of type meant enough lines to make about two inches in depth. In editorial-office parlance it still means a one-column story about two inches deep. Similarly, a *galley* means about 20 column inches; it is frequently used when a *column* is meant, since average newspaper columns also are 20 inches long.

Type sizes.—In describing a type face the size always must be stated as well as the name of the type itself. Sizes are stated always in points. The size of a type is understood to be the size of the smallest body that will accommodate that particular size of the face.

MMMMMMMMMMMMMM

FIG. 15.—Range of the common type sizes, 6-point to 72-point (Garamond Oldstyle Roman).

It will be seen later in connection with machine composition that the width of the "shoulder" may be increased to provide more space between lines. In such a case we may have "8-point type on a 10-point body," or whatever the case may be. In foundry type, however, it is the rule always to cast each face on the smallest possible body size. The compositor then inserts leads if additional space is desired between lines. Most types are made in sizes which range from 6-point to 72-point. The more usual point-sizes are as follows: 6, 8, 10, 12, 14, 18, 24, 30, 36, 42, 48, 60, and 72.

Book publishers use intermediate sizes of 7-, 9-, 11-, and 16-point. Machine faces include odd display sizes, such as 21-, 28-, and 34-point. Caslon No. 471 has a 22-point size.

Newspapers lately have adopted, in addition to the "agate" size already mentioned, certain "bastard" sizes. These have been introduced in connection with the redesigned newspaper faces of high legibility. The sizes are 6¼-, 6¾-, 7¼-, and 7½-point.

In some plain faces, sizes as small as 5-, 4½-, and even 4-point are available. In display types, very large sizes are cast in metal, ranging upward from 72-point to 84-, 96-, 120-, and 144-point.

Poster printers use wood type—letters cut in type-high, end-grain blocks. Wood type is specified as to size by the height of the capital letters, stated in picas, or *pica lines*. Thus it is referred to as "5-line," "8-line," and so on.

Wood type has no shoulder. Many of the larger sizes of metal type also are cast without shoulder. This saves metal. Descending letters are cast on larger bodies than the others of the same font. Blank spacing materials are used to supply the place of shoulders.

Types used for "banner" or "strip" headings usually are capital letters cast without shoulders; otherwise there would be a wide area of white space between a large headline and the type lines below it.

Determining type size of printed specimen.—One of the most elementary type problems that arises is to determine the size *body type* in which the text matter of something has been printed. This is how printers do it: A specimen consisting of at least a dozen lines is examined. Some instance is found in which a descending letter in one line and an ascending letter in the line below come close together in a vertical line. If they almost touch each other, the lines are determined to be *solid*—no extra space (*lead*) has been inserted between lines.

If there is space between the two characters, its amount can be estimated. It usually will be one point or two points, in which case the eye readily can distinguish which it is. If the space is more than this, however, it may be necessary to measure it with a printer's line gauge.

Next, the number of printed lines to the inch of depth is ascertained. To do this accurately it is best to count the lines included in several inches of column depth. Then, calling 72 points an inch, the depth in points is calculated and this figure is divided by the number of counted lines. In nearly every case, if the work is accurate, the quotient will be an integral number of points.

If the type has been set solid, this number is the point-size of the type under consideration. If the page is *leaded*, that is, if space has been provided for between lines, the amount of this space, as determined above, must be deducted from the number of points each line occupies in the specimen in order to ascertain the point-size of the type itself.

10-point Memphis
Medium solid

To such an extent have the signs representing sounds been multiplied, that many of the letters are pronounced in several different ways. . . . . Indeed it is computed that many words of no more than two syllables may be spelled in several thousand different modes, by the use of combinations actually employed in other words in the (English) language. The word *scissors*, for instance, may be thus written in nearly six thousand different ways.—*Webster*

10-point Memphis
Medium 1-point
leaded

To such an extent have the signs representing sounds been multiplied, that many of the letters are pronounced in several different ways. . . . . Indeed it is computed that many words of no more than two syllables may be spelled in several thousand different modes, by the use of combinations actually employed in other words in the (English) language. The word *scissors*, for instance, may be thus written in nearly six thousand different ways.—*Webster*

10-point Memphis
Medium 2-point
leaded

To such an extent have the signs representing sounds been multiplied, that many of the letters are pronounced in several different ways. . . . . Indeed it is computed that many words of no more than two syllables may be spelled in several thousand different modes, by the use of combinations actually employed in other words in the (English) language. The word *scissors*, for instance, may be thus written in nearly six thousand different ways.—*Webster*

FIG. 16.—Type lines set solid, and leaded one point, and two points

Here is an example set in Caslon Old Face:

> The student of type faces must early recognize that the
> point-size is not readily determined, even by the expert
> user of types. The variation in the apparent size of the
> specimen lines in this book is marked. Yet all the lines
> are 24-point size. The only safe way is to measure and
> compare with known specimens of the same or similar
> types. The student of type faces must early recognize
> that the point-size is not readily determined, even by the
> expert user of types. The variation in the apparent size

Examine the third and fourth lines, left-hand side. The *p*
in the third line is almost exactly over the *l* in the line below.
The two letters do not quite touch, however. There is about one
point between them.

Now measure the depth of the paragraph and count the
lines. It contains 9 lines and measures almost exactly one and
one-half inches, or 108 points, in over-all depth. Dividing 108
by 9 shows that each line of the specimen occupies 12 points
depth. But there is an added point between lines; deducting
this we decide that the paragraph is set in 11-point type. It is
therefore stated to be 11-point leaded with one-point leads (or
set on a 12-point body).

Estimating copy.—One of the commonest problems involving type measurement is that of ascertaining how much space
a given typewritten manuscript will occupy in a specified type.
Or the problem may be to determine what type-size should be
specified if the copy is to fit a certain space. As a corollary to
both problems it may be necessary to find out how much copy
to write for a given space and a specified type-size. Because
types vary greatly in width, rule-of-thumb methods of estimating how much space copy will occupy which use as a basis the
number of words to the square inch or to the column never can
be even reasonably exact.

There have been and are many methods suggested for handling this problem and its corollaries. One method notably combines accuracy with simplicity. For its purposes simple tables are available giving detailed data of character counts for most type faces. These tables, of which a sample is shown below, give the average number of letters and spaces which will occupy a line of any given length, when copy is set in any specified size of the face named.

For example, a line 26 picas wide set in 12-point Caslon Old Face is found, by reference to the table, to contain on the average 62 letters and spaces. Similarly a line of 8-point 26 picas wide of this type will provide room for 90 letters and spaces.

CASLON OLD FACE*

Width in picas	1	10	12	14	16	18	20	22	24	26	28	30	32	34	36
6 Point	4.05	41	49	57	65	73	81	89	97	105	113	122	130	138	146
8 Point	3.45	35	41	48	55	62	69	76	83	90	97	104	110	117	124
9 Point	3.1	31	37	43	50	56	62	68	74	81	87	93	99	105	112
10 Point	3.	30	36	42	48	54	60	66	72	78	84	90	96	102	108
11 Point	2.75	28	33	39	44	50	55	61	66	72	77	83	88	94	99
11½ Point	2.55	26	31	36	41	46	51	56	61	66	71	77	82	87	92
12 Point	2.4	24	29	34	38	43	48	53	58	62	67	72	77	82	86
14 Point	2.15	22	26	30	34	39	43	47	52	56	60	65	69	73	77
18 Point	1.9	19	23	27	30	34	38	42	46	49	53	57	61	65	68

* Table, from *Mergenthaler Copy-fitting Chart*, to be used in determining number of letters of a given size of Caslon Old Face that will occupy any specified length of line.

The number of letters and spaces in a typewritten manuscript is found quite accurately by multiplying the average number of letters and spaces in one line by the number of lines. "Pica" typewriter has 10 characters to the inch; "Elite" has 12 characters.

In such computations it is customary to count all lines as full lines. This allows usually for the extra space needed for paragraphs and around headings.

Having determined the number of letters and spaces in the copy by means of the tables, it is easy to solve the copy-fitting problem in any of its four general forms:

I. *To find out how many lines the copy will make when set in type*, given (1) the size and kind of type and (2) the width of lines, or measure: From the table find out how many characters of the specified type will go in a line of the given width. Divide the total number of characters in the copy by the number of characters in one line of the type. This will give the number of type lines.

Given the number of type lines, the depth in inches can be calculated from the following table:

6-point—12 lines to the inch	11-point—6½ lines (approx.)
7-point—10 lines (approx.)	12-point— 6 lines
8-point— 9 lines	14-point— 5 lines (approx.)
9-point— 8 lines	18-point— 4 lines
10-point— 7 lines (approx.)	24-point— 3 lines

II. *To find what size type to use if the copy must fit a given space:* By inspection, decide upon a size that seems likely to be right. Determine how many lines of this size will go in the given depth of type space. Find from the table how many characters of this size and kind of type will go in a line of the specified width.

Multiply these two numbers together.

If the product is less than the number of characters in the copy, try a smaller size. If the product is greater than the number of characters in the copy, a larger size is indicated.

Sometimes one size will be too small but the next size will be too large. In such cases leading between lines must be resorted to in order to make the smaller size of type fit the space.

III. *To write exactly enough copy to fit a specified space when set in a given size and kind of type:* First, ascertain from the table how many characters of the specified type will go in a line of the given width. Next determine how many lines of

type will be required for the given depth. Then set the typewriter line-stops to a length of typewritten line which contains
the number of characters needed for a type line. Write the
required number of lines. The type matter will run line for line
with the typewriting.

There is a deep-felt sense of peace and
quietude that fills the inner consciousness of
everyone who employs his hands at simple,
skillful work. This tranquil sense seems to
reach its zenith in the cheerful task of setting type out of a printer's case.

12-point Typewriter

There is a deep-felt sense of peace and
quietude that fills the inner consciousness of
everyone who employs his hands at simple,
skillful work. This tranquil sense seems to
reach its zenith in the cheerful task of setting type out of a printer's case.

10-point Typewriter

There is a deep-felt sense of peace and
quietude that fills the inner consciousness of
everyone who employs his hands at simple,
skillful work. This tranquil sense seems to
reach its zenith in the cheerful task of setting type out of a printer's case.

10-point Bodoni Book justified

FIG. 17.—Typewritten lines compared with type-set lines. The first
six lines above show Pica typewriting; next the same lines appear in
Elite typewriting; finally they are shown as a justified paragraph of
10-point Bodoni Book.

For example, a reporter or a copyreader might be called
upon to write a story to accompany an illustration, to occupy an
adjoining column, and to be exactly the same depth as the pic-
ture. Let us say that this is six inches.

The story is to be set, say, in one column, 12 picas wide, in

8-point Ionic No. 5 solid. Eight-point runs 9 lines to the inch. This means that 54 lines will be required for the six inches of column depth. A 12-pica line of 8-point Ionic No. 5 contains 32 characters. Therefore the typewriter should be set to produce lines that average 32 characters, and 54 of these lines should be written to fill the given space exactly.

IV. *To find how much space copy which has been printed in one size will occupy when reset in a larger or smaller size:* This is similar to Problem I, above. It involves, however, use of the table for the given type to determine the character count. Say the copy has been set in 6-point Bodoni 12 picas wide and that there are 10 lines of it. How many lines will it make set in 8-point Textype?

Reference to a table for 6-point Bodoni gives an average of 47 characters to a 12-pica line. There are therefore 470 characters in the 10 lines. In a 12-pica line of 8-point Textype there are 35 characters on an average. Therefore, the copy when reset in this type will occupy 470 divided by 35, or 14 lines.

If copy-fitting tables are not available, several lines of a given specimen of type should be counted to the desired line length to ascertain the character count.

Type composition is accurate.—In any discussion of accuracy an engineer asks, "What are the limits of tolerance?" Printers work very accurately, considering the comparative softness of their materials. Examining their product we see that this must be so.

Consider a page of type. It is made up of thousands of small pieces of metal. These are fitted together so accurately that with only a few wrappings of cord and the pressure of the fingers the whole page can be lifted safely. In book work 16, 32, or even 64 pages are assembled in units. Pressure from small sliding wedges (called *quoins*) serves to hold the whole together in a rigid *form.* When a form is *locked,* the whole must be so accurate that it is not possible to withdraw a single letter from its place. The test of a perfect assembly is to apply strong vertical pressure to the pages of type; any imperfection of workmanship will be detected instantly.

Here let the word *justification* be noticed. Printers use this word, with its verb form *to justify*, in many ways. Principally it carries the broad sense of *making even*, with connotations of accuracy and skillful workmanship. When foundry type is set, each line must be accurately spaced to exact length, either by increasing the spacing between words, or by placing spaces and quads at one or both ends of the lines. This is *justification*. Similarly the spacing out of columns to even depth also is justification. Any operation in printing that involves bringing type and spacing materials together with exactness is described by this term.

The limit of tolerance in any operation is the thinnest piece of material available to the workman. In printing, this is a half-point space, which measures a little less than seven-thousandths of an inch. These thin spaces, made of copper, are used for final justification of the type line.

The student should examine a half-point space in order to comprehend just how closely printers work. It should be noted, however, that in the larger metropolitan newspaper composing rooms, where all pages are converted by the stereotyping process into solid, curved plates, very accurate spacing is not necessary. Under such circumstances, the pages are not lifted but are slid from make-up truck to matrix press.

CHAPTER FOUR

Type Composition by Hand

Why type is set by hand; printers' case and composing sticks; learning the case; characters easily confused; printers' style; proofs, corrections, and distribution

WHY set type by hand? Each year typesetting machines are being improved in ways that permit them to take over a greater share of the business of putting words into print. Bigger machine types and a wider range of faces have now made it possible for the printer to set almost anything on composing machines. Yet, paradoxically enough, the production of foundry type, made to be set by hand, is greater today than ever before—even greater in tonnage than it was before machines were invented, when all type was set by hand.

The explanation of this paradox is to be found in the fact that users of printing have become type-conscious. There is a continual demand for variety, for individuality, for something new; and every new type instantly is seized upon by advertisers and other users of printing. This means that yesterday's types quickly are relegated to the metal pot and the cases which held them are refilled with the latest creations in type metal.

Everyone seems to gain something from this state of affairs. Certainly for the type merchant it is good business. Advertisers also gain by the increased attractiveness and the "modern" appearance of their appeals in print. And the printer who keeps abreast of the type-times gains important selling advantages.

Even the general public is becoming aware of good typography, and where advertisements once were skipped over they now are examined with appreciation of their typographic attractiveness; and the advertiser thereby gets an extra dividend on his investment in new type and better typography.

This is why hand-set advertisements and hand-set headings continue to hold their own against all the inroads of type "technocracy." There is, of course, always the possibility that some new and revolutionary invention will do away with type altogether. In the opinion of most printers and technical men, however, type will be set by hand for many generations to come.

Experience is valuable.—It is important, then, that every student of publishing or advertising know about hand composition. He needs to have a feeling for type—to know both its tremendous possibilities and its limitations. To acquire this there is no better way—certainly no more direct and stimulating way—than to set type. If it is only a few lines or a small page, it gives one a thrill, and a sense of achievement. Not a few great journalists and other men of importance have learned to set type in their youth and have in later life operated small private presses for fun. There is probably no more satisfying hobby.

Learn to set type.—Let us put a composing stick in the hand of the student and a case of good type before him, and let him learn what the art has to teach him. He will learn patience, for one thing. He will learn, too, what constitutes good spacing, and will come to perceive other aspects of printing "style." One thing is certain. He will never be accused, as newcomers to journalism and advertising so often are, of thinking that type is made of rubber. He will know that when a line is full, not another letter, not even "a little, thin one," can be added.

Best of all, he will make mistakes in type and will have to

correct them. He will omit a necessary word perhaps, a little word—only two or three letters—at the beginning of a long paragraph of type. Discovering the omission, he will then twist and he will squirm. He will wish to high heaven that he might change the copy. But in the end he will have to lift out and run over and re-space every line of that paragraph, down to the very last one. Never again will he make a change in a proof, no matter how necessary, without remembering the wearisome task that was his. He will prepare carefully any copy for which he is responsible. And in dealing with proof he will withhold the blue pencil or, if he must make a change, he will take out or add words so that only a line or two will have to be reset. Then the Linotype operator or the hand compositor will look at that proof and will say to himself, or perhaps to the world: "There's a fellow who knows his business."

How type is set.—As has been well said, the best way to learn to do a thing is to do it. So it is with type. No description can take the place of actual experience at the case. Students are therefore advised to accompany the reading of this description with actual practice.

Let us look at the case. It is a wooden tray, 32 inches long, 17 inches wide, and almost two inches deep. This is divided into compartments of various sizes. Large compartments or boxes are provided for letters which occur frequently, and smaller boxes for the others.

Formerly, when straight matter—that is, the column matter of newspapers and the text matter of books—was set by hand, two cases were required to hold the large fonts used. One of these cases held the capitals and small capitals, the other the small letters. The two cases were supported on a frame, one above the other. The lower case was for small letters; and these are still called *lower-case* letters. This case sloped up from the compositor at a slight angle, so that he might have a clear view of the contents of each box.

The *cap* case was supported above and behind the lower case, sloping upward at a greater angle. This arrangement made it possible for the compositor both to see into each box and to reach into any without leaning forward or otherwise changing his position. The average distance from box to stick was about 14 inches.

Many "comps" worked sitting on a high stool; but others preferred to stand directly in front of the large box containing spaces, which is slightly to the left of center in the lower case. It was unnecessary for the workman to move about or to shift his feet from this position in order to reach any letter.

The California case.—Today these two cases, which were called *news* cases, are combined into one, with the caps at the right and the lower-case letters at the left. This combination has been worked out in many ways, to include room for various

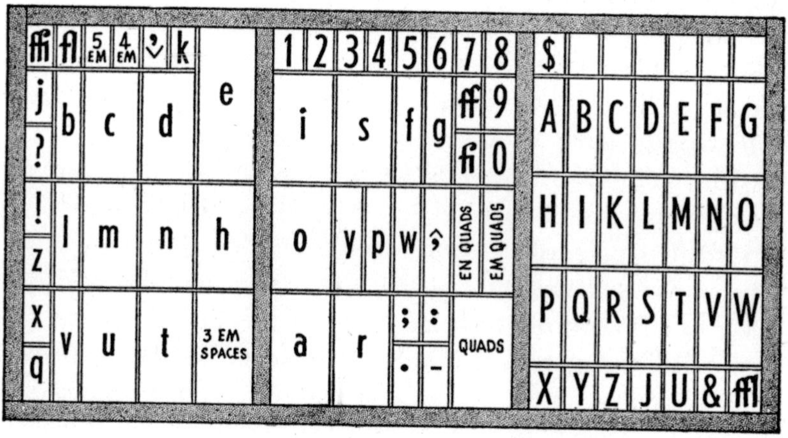

Fig. 18.—Layout of the California job case

special characters; but the great majority of cases used throughout the United States are on the model known as the *California job case*. Its layout is shown in the accompanying diagram. It is the only case layout the student needs to know.

Plan of the case.—The capitals follow a simple scheme. Passing over the small boxes in the top row, which are used for special characters, such as the dollar sign and parentheses, we find capital *A* in the box at the left of the second row, *B* in the next box on the right, and *C* in the next. The rest of the letters follow in alphabetical order in horizontal rows. Cap *Z* is in the third box from the left in the lower row. But where are *J* and *U?* They do not appear in the alphabetical arrangement. Thereby hangs a tale.

Like all type affairs, the type case is very old—over four hundred years old. When the first "cap" case was laid out, there were only twenty-four letters in the English alphabet. The letters *I* and *V* did double duty, each serving as both consonant and vowel. This was sometimes confusing, and therefore, a century or so later, variants of these two characters came into use—*J* for consonant *I*, and *U* for the vowel sound of *V*.

Changes in familiar things are always awkward; and the new letters, as they slowly came into use, were not thrust willy-nilly into the well-remembered order of existing cases but were placed following the letter *Z*. And there they are today.

The lower-case layout is ancient, too. Modern "improvements" have not changed it. Just as the standard typewriter keyboard is planned to permit the striking of much-used combinations of letters with a single hand movement, the printer's lower case is laid out to bring many of these combinations together. More than this, the boxes are so arranged that the letters most frequently used are nearest to the stick. It is often a shock to a modern student of manual efficiency to find that the printers of four centuries ago worked out a highly efficient arrangement for the boxes of the type case.

There is little advantage to be gained by the student's memorizing the position of the lower-case letters in their order. He should, however, make for himself a copy of the case layout on a piece of cardboard four or five inches long. This card can then be laid on the case for ready reference while he is setting his first type. When approached in this way, "learning the case" is easy.

The composing stick.—So much for the case. Next the student needs a composing stick. There are many kinds of sticks. The first ones were carved from an actual stick of wood. They could be used to set lines of only one width—one *measure*. Modern sticks are of metal, with a movable "knee," and most of them are accurately graduated to pica and half-pica settings.

The stick having been set to the desired measure, it is grasped in the left hand, open edge up. The back of the stick rests partly in the palm of the hand, partly across the base of the fingers. The thumb extends over the front edge of the stick, and holds the letters upright as they are set.

The composing rule.—It is essential to have a smooth surface for the type to rest against while the line is being assembled and justified. For this purpose a *composing rule*

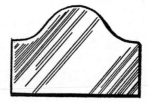

Fig. 19.—Composing rule; also make-up rule

sometimes is used. This is a thin strip of steel or brass, usually two points thick, equal in width to the line which is being set. Small projections at the ends of the composing rule serve for lifting it out after a line is completed. A lead, a slug, or a type-high brass rule of the proper length may serve the same purpose.

Spaces and quads.—Next let us examine the *spaces*, which are used between words, and the *quads*, which serve to fill out wider blank portions of lines, such as occur at the beginning or end of a paragraph.

Spaces are named according to their em-relationship. The normal space is 3-to-em, that is, three of these spaces placed side by side make up the width of an em of the type with which they are used. Other spaces are 4-to-em, 5-to-em, and 6-to-em, the last often called *hair spaces*.

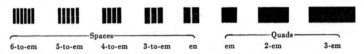

Fig. 20.—Diagram to show the relationship between the various sizes of 12-point spaces and quads.

By using various combinations of the standard spaces it is possible to make up almost any intermediate width and so to solve any justification problem. In most commercial composition, however, when spaces between words are to be increased slightly, brass 1-point or copper ½-point spaces are used. Most commercial printing offices provide plenty of these handy, time-saving spaces.

As has been noted, newspaper offices ordinarily do not require great accuracy in spacing. For this reason brass and copper spaces seldom are found in newspaper composing rooms.

Starting composition.—At the beginning of a paragraph the first thing to be placed in the stick, in the lower left corner, against the composing rule or slug, is a quad for the paragraph indention. Every blank space in every line of type must be represented as a piece of metal—not just skipped as in typewriting. Most composition requires an em quad for indention, all paragraphs in the same matter being indented uniformly.

Next the capital letter which starts the first sentence is lifted from its box and placed alongside the quad. The nick should be uppermost. This means that the face of the letter reads upside down, and the top of the letter is toward the compositor; but as the letters are assembled in the stick the line reads from left to right in the normal fashion.

At first the type letters look strange in their reversed and upside-down position, but soon the compositor is able to read them quite as readily as he reads printed lines. It is important for the young journalist to learn to read type in this way. In supervising page make-up the ability will stand him in good stead.

Letter by letter—oh, so slowly at first—the line of type grows. Usually, a normal, 3-to-em (3-em for short) space is inserted between words when the line is being assembled. Perhaps the last word does not quite fill the line, or this word is too long for the space available to receive it: If the first, the line must be spaced out to fill; if the latter, the spaces between words may be reduced; or, if this is not practicable, the last word must be divided, a hyphen being placed conveniently after a syllable, and the word completed in the next line.

In either case, then, the final step is to increase (or, sometimes, to decrease) the space between words, so that the completed line will fill the measure accurately. This is called *justifying* the line.

Good justification has a significance that may not be immediately apparent to the beginner. If all lines are not of the same length, the longer ones will hold the pressure off the short ones, and these short lines will fall out when a page is lifted or, worse yet, will get off their feet—that is, they will lean sidewise in the line and only portions of their faces will show in the proof.

The test of a well-justified line is simple: It should not bind between the jaws of the stick, so as to need force to lift it out. On the other hand, the line should fit firmly enough so that it will not fall back when it is pushed forward in the stick. These are the accepted mechanical tests of good spacing.

The appearance of a line in the proof affords another and quite different test of spacing. Spacing between words always should appear uniform. Experience shows that tall, straight letters dwarf the spaces alongside them. Contrariwise, small, round letters make adjacent spaces seem wider. A careful compositor will study his proofs to see if the spacing gives an impression to the eye of being uniform. This is one of those niceties of composition which causes collectors of fine books to prefer those set by hand to those set by machine. It is entirely possible, of course, to do beautiful spacing when setting type on a composing machine. As a rule, however, the finer points of spacing within lines are ignored in machine-set matter on account of the extra cost involved. The primary purpose of the machine is to set type rapidly and at low cost.

Picking up letters.—A good compositor looks ahead of his hand into the box from which he will take the next letter. His eye selects a letter, noting its position; he then picks up that letter and no other in the box. Having seen where the nicks are, he turns the letter in his fingers to bring it right-end up and with the nicks away from him, and all the while his hand is traveling in a continuous motion to the stick. He does not look at the letter again during this movement; his eyes have gone on to select the next letter.

An occasional gentle shaking of the case forward and back a few times helps in composition, since the letters in the boxes are thereby coaxed to assume more or less uniformly vertical positions and may be more easily handled into the stick.

Reading the stick.—When a line is complete, and before the compositor justifies it, he should read it over. This is called "reading the stick." Any wrongly turned types as well as wrong letters and other errors should be detected at this stage and corrected immediately. Otherwise the proof will be "dirty" and the job of making corrections will be a lengthy one.

In learning to read the stick the compositor should pay particular attention to the lower-case letters *b*, *d*, *q*, and *p*. These are confusing at first, in their upside-down and reversed positions. The difficulty is solved by noticing that the bowl, or round part of each of these, properly turns in the same direction, right

(b, p) or left (d, q) whether viewed as type or in the printed page.

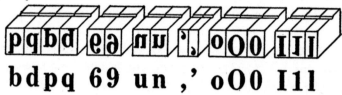

bdpq 69 un ,' oO0 I1l

Fig. 21.—Because these characters confuse the typesetting beginner, they are often called "devils" or "demons." The upper row represents the letters as they appear in the composing stick; the lower row shows how they appear in print.

Some notes on typesetting and spacing.—Close spacing between words is to be preferred to wide. In testing spacing, proofs are turned upside down; all the inequalities of spacing, the "rivers" of white, then appear.

Types with long descenders require less word-spacing than others. The reason is simple. A 12-point Caslon Old Face, for example, is no larger, except for its descenders, than an ordinary 10-point type. When setting these types, many typographers use 4-em spaces. The usual box for these 4-em spaces is small— too small to contain enough to replace the normal 3-em spaces. Dividing the regular 3-em space box diagonally with a strip of wood solves this problem: The 4-em spaces are placed above, and the 3-em below, this dividing strip.

Paragraphs should not be indented any more than is necessary to make them easily distinguishable from other text lines. In narrow measures an em-quad may be too much. Two 3-em spaces or a 3-em space with an en-quad will look much better. This is especially true of the long-descender faces.

A good rule is: Decrease the space after commas and quotation marks; increase a little after a question mark or an interrogation point; also increase after a colon or a semicolon. In most cases a normal space should follow a period and precede the capital letter that starts a new sentence. Exceptions occur

in the case of cap *T*, cap *V*, and others which carry their own
extra space next to a preceding period. Here the space before
the capital can be reduced or even omitted in closely spaced
lines.

Most modern types have a thin shoulder on the left of the
question mark, interrogation point, colon, and semicolon. This
avoids the extra work of inserting a thin space before these
characters, as was formerly necessary.

Space at the end of a paragraph should never be less than
one em; if it is, the last line should be spaced out to a full line.
In spacing out a short line with quads, place the justifying spaces
next to the type. This helps in distribution.

Fitting and set of letters.—In designing type faces, the
peculiarities of each separate letter must be studied with regard
to all other letters which may adjoin it on either side in forming
words. In most fonts appreciable spaces will be noticed on one
or both sides of the individual type letters which have the effect
of separating them in the line. If a font of fairly large type is
examined, it will be seen that these spaces are not uniform.
There may be more space on one side of a letter than on the
other. Some letters extend to the edge of the body on one or
both sides.

This internal spacing of types may vary in amount as well
as in specific detail. The relationship of the face width to the
body width determines the *set* of a type font.

The positions of the individual letters on their respective
bodies determine another type quality, called its *fitting*. The
terms *set* and *fitting* are interrelated. The more closely types are
set, the more attention the typefounder must give to their fitting.
Changing the set of a face noticeably alters its character. A
beautiful type is always found to be well-fitted, so that there
are no awkward gaps between letters.

Thin spaces, ranging in thickness from $\frac{1}{2}$ point up to 2
points or more, often are placed between the letters of words.

This is called *letterspacing,* and may be done for several reasons. In lines of all-capitals, the fitting of the letters always is
inexact, since the typefounder adjusts these letters specifically
for use with lower-case. In lines consisting of caps only, it therefore is necessary to correct the faults of spacing between the
characters by adding thin spaces of different thicknesses according to the capitals involved. Between capitals which have
vertical sides, extra space is needed. Between angular strokes,
no spacing is necessary. The following specimen illustrates
this with an example of bad fitting of capitals, and the same
line letterspaced to correct the fitting.

MULTANE   MULTANE

Fig. 22.—Letterspacing is highly desirable in lines of capitals to correct the inequalities of spacing between letters.

Letterspacing is used frequently in setting headlines, in
order to lengthen short lines and to make heads more symmetrical. It is not to be encouraged as a regular practice, for two
reasons: first, it takes time to insert the letterspaces, especially
in machine composition; and, second, headings look better if
they are not letterspaced.

Sometimes whole lines of type, such as legends, or short
paragraphs in which a decorative effect is desired, are letterspaced throughout. As has been said, this changes the whole
character of the type face, giving it a feeling of formality or a
hand-lettered appearance.

In German and some other foreign languages, letterspacing
of words takes the place of italics for emphasis.

Division of words.—The dictionary should be consulted
on word divisions. There is an explanation of the principles of
this important and involved subject in the introductory pages
of most dictionaries. These principles of syllabification are intricate, and even the lexicographers do not always agree. There-

fore one should keep a small, authoritative dictionary at hand when setting type, and all doubts should be resolved by reference to it.

Emptying the stick; the galley.—An ordinary stick will hold 12 to 14 lines of newspaper type. When the stick is full, it becomes necessary to remove the "stickful" and to place the newly composed lines on a galley.

Galleys are brass or steel trays of various shapes and sizes, surrounded on three sides by a rim about two-thirds of type-height. A galley is placed on the working top so that, as the compositor stands facing the galley, its closed end is toward his right.

The working top usually slopes upward to prevent the end letters of type lines from falling down. Newspaper ad men and catalogue compositors, however, prefer to work on a flat surface, using a metal bar to support the open side of the composition.

To lift the type into a galley the compositor places his stick on the case, with a slug or composing rule at the back, above the first line. Following the last line set he places a blank slug—a strip of space-high metal, usually six points thick, and the same length as the lines. He now has the type between two firm surfaces. Pressing his thumbs against the composing rule or slug at the closed side of the stick and his forefingers against the slug at the open side, he tips the lines out of the stick with a rolling motion upward, bringing his thumbs up first.

As he does so he keeps the end letters in place with his bent middle fingers. A full stick of type, even when the lines are quite long, can be lifted in this way and placed on the galley without hazard.

Beginners sometimes open the stick by moving back the adjustable knee before starting to lift the type it contains. This almost always results in "pied" type. (For some reason lost in the dim past, printers call type that has fallen down in disorder *pi.*) The stick, once set, should not be opened.

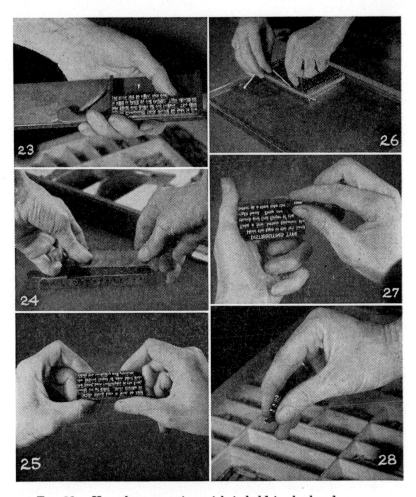

FIG. 23.—How the composing stick is held in the hand.

FIG. 24.—A single line or a stickful of type may be lifted out of the stick by grasping it firmly as shown in this illustration.

FIG. 25.—Lines of type when being lifted and carried are held firmly with pressure exerted against ends as well as top and bottom.

FIG. 26.—A short length of cotton cord is used to tie up type lines for proofing. Four or five turns are enough. The loose end is secured by tucking it behind the wrapped strands.

FIG. 27.—Illustration to show how type is held in the hand while it is being distributed.

FIG. 28.—The fingers separate the type letters and drop them, one at a time, into their proper boxes in the case.

Tying a page.—It is unlikely that our beginner will set a full galley of newspaper type. If he did, before pulling a proof, he would block the lines firmly in the galley with a wooden side stick. Smaller amounts of type, however, are usually tied with cotton cord.

Here is the procedure for tying type firmly:

Examine the lines to see that all types are firm on their feet and, if the composition is leaded, that no letter has slipped past the leads. Now take enough plain cotton twine to encircle the type matter four or five times.

Start at the lower right-hand corner. Place the end of the twine so that a little more than an inch overlaps this corner. Hold it in this position with the thumb and forefinger of the left hand.

With the right hand draw the string clockwise around the type. When you reach the lower left corner, cross over the short end there, and draw the first turn up snugly.

Continue on around again, this time exerting a firm pull on the twine, and crossing the short end again when you reach it; repeat two or three more times, until the other end of the string is reached.

Now lay a loop of the end of the string in a position near a corner where it can be pushed behind all the layers with the ear of the composing rule. Hold the last turn tight with the fingers of the left hand while the loop is being formed and pushed down. Last of all, draw the loop down and back until it binds against the layers where they turn the corner. Leave the free end of the cord where it can be grasped readily in untying the page.

Pulling a proof.—After being tied, the type is carried on the galley to the proof press and placed on its bed. Care should be exercised by the student at this point. Some proof presses require that the type be removed from the galley and placed directly on the iron bed of the press. Other presses have a removable false bed of the same thickness as the bottom of a galley. This is used when pulling proofs of plates or large pages and must be removed from the press before placing a galley upon the bed; if the thickness of a galley is added to that of the false bed, the proof press will be damaged and the type which is being proofed will be destroyed.

In this as in other unfamiliar circumstances around a composing room, the best rule is, "Ask first." Or, if there is no one present to answer questions, turn the proof-press roller up to the type very slowly. If it does not move easily over the first line, do not force it, but slide the page off the galley and try again. Only a moderate amount of pressure upon the operating crank is needed to rotate the printing cylinder of a modern precision proof press.

Hand proofs.—Not all proofs are pulled on proof presses. Some small shops do not have them, and all but the largest newspapers proof full pages and large advertisements by hand. Sometimes these hand-pulled proofs are called "planer" proofs.

Hand-proofing is simple, and yet calls for some skill. The type, as it lies on a stone or other firm surface, is inked in the usual manner. For a "dry" hand proof such as most printers use, a sheet of thin paper made especially for this purpose—smooth on one side and rough on the other—is laid on the form, smooth side toward the type, care being taken that the sheet does not move after it once touches the inked page. Over this first sheet a second sheet is laid, likewise smooth side down. (The top sheet of paper operates to prevent shifting the bottom sheet when the planer is lifted and moved.) Next a proof planer (a wooden block covered with heavy felt) is laid on one corner of the sheet and is struck a firm blow with a wooden mallet or a bar of metal. The planer then is lifted, moved to an adjacent area, and struck again. The procedure is repeated until the entire page has been covered. The two sheets of paper may now be lifted slowly from the type and the bottom one should bear a readable proof of the page.

A somewhat clearer proof may be secured by first wetting a sheet of proof paper with a sponge and laying it dry side down on the type. The planer may be used on such a sheet directly. Wetting the paper before proofing helps to make a clear impression, but such proof must be dried before it can be used.

Inking and washing type.—It is well to remember, in inking type, that too much ink is worse than not enough. A thin film of ink should cover the face of the type evenly and completely.

Fig. 29.—Inking roller, or brayer, used in pulling hand proofs

Ink, which is really a high grade of oil paint, dries in a short time to a hard coating. It should always be removed from type immediately after the proof is pulled. For this purpose a soft cloth is provided. With a corner of this cloth barely saturated with printers' solvent, the ink can readily be removed from the type surface; then the dry portion of the cloth should be used to remove any surplus solvent.

If ink dries on type, it must be removed with a stronger solvent similar to paint remover, because fresh ink will not adhere to a surface which is covered with dried ink.

When type is being cleaned after pulling a proof, excess solvent must not be allowed to flow down into the type; evaporation under such conditions will be slow, and the gasoline vapor will prevent pulling another good proof for some time; also the excess solvent will carry ink between the type to harden and render the type dirty and difficult to distribute.

Correcting the proof.—We will assume that the proof has been read and marked and that the student compositor is to correct his errors. Until he is experienced, he will do well to place the type on the galley and to lift into the stick separately each line in which a correction is to be made. After being corrected, and re-justified if necessary, the lines are replaced in the galley. In this way accurate justification, the great importance of which has been explained, will be maintained.

Revises.—After the corrections indicated in a proof have been made, it is customary to pull another proof. This is called a *revise*. The original proof and the revise are then returned to the proofreader for comparison or, as it is called, *revising*.

If uncorrected or new errors appear in the revise, a second revise may be necessary. Sometimes changes from copy, or other conditions, call for a third revise, or even a fourth or fifth. The rule in many places is to continue the revising process until the proof is *O.K.*, or "clear." On most newspapers, if only one or two errors are marked on a proof, the one who corrects the type checks the corrections carefully and sends the galley along on his own responsibility.

Distributing type.—After foundry type has been used, it must be returned to the case. This procedure is called *distribution*. For ease in handling, the type may be moistened by untying it on a galley and applying a wet sponge to its surface, thus slightly loosening the lines so as to permit the water to penetrate between the letters.

Ten or twelve lines at a time may now be lifted from the galley while being held firmly in the same fashion as when the lines were lifted from the stick.

Held thus, the block of type should be turned in the fingers until it rests on the top slug. Each letter then lies horizontally.

Now the thumb and middle finger of the left hand are shifted to hold the end letters in place. The right hand is thus freed to take up the task of distributing the letters.

Taking off the last slug, the distributor picks up, between his right thumb, forefinger, and middle finger, a portion of the last line at the right. His hand now moves over the case and drops the letters and spaces into their respective boxes. The letters of each word are distributed in order, so that the word is "spelled" mentally in distributing it.

Care must be taken to return letters always to their right boxes. Failure to do so results in a pied or "dirty" case and makes extra work for the person who next sets type from it.

Proofreading.—Most people assume quite erroneously that reading proof requires no special aptitude or training. Those who have tried it, however, discover that the finding of misspelled words is but a small part of the work of the proof-reader. He must pass upon matters of capitalization, punctuation, sentence construction, and typography. Moreover, he is expected to introduce the element of consistency into the proofs that pass his pencil. If the author spells it "catalogue" on page 2, he may not be allowed to spell it "catalog" on page 102. There are thousands of these niceties which must be known to the proofreader, and he must be alert in order that none of them may "get by" him.

It is beyond the purpose and scope of this book to teach even the rudiments of proofreading. Almost any desk-reference book or any dictionary will give the student specimens of proof-reader's marks with their uses illustrated. Then there are proofreading manuals, and printers' style books, which specify in detail all matters of capitalization, punctuation, spacing, division of words, use of italics and small capitals, and hundreds of other matters of proofreading.

Style books.—Printing "style" is an intricate subject. This is quite a different thing from literary style, with which journalists have so much to do. Most newspapers have a style book which covers matters of capitalization, punctuation, spelling, and abbreviations. It is the proofreader's Bible, and enables the editorial department, the compositors, and the proofroom to work in harmony.

A great many matters of style apply only to typesetting. They do not enter into writing or typewriting. The student will gain much by a careful reading of a good style book, such as that of the University of Chicago Press—*A Manual of Style.* He probably will be astonished at the many niceties of printed language that are revealed in its pages.

Reading proof, as an occupation, is less humdrum than is sometimes supposed, and not a little of the integrity of civilization turns upon its efficient performance.

CHAPTER FIVE

Rules, Borders, and Dashes

Elements of the printed page other than type; ornaments and special characters; decorative initial letters; furniture and other spacing materials

Besides the letters of the various type alphabets which make up printed pages, many other devices and characters are made for use with type. With some of these the student will need more than a bowing acquaintance, if type is to work for him.

Brass and metal rules.—Probably the most important adjuncts to type are *rules*, the lines which separate columns of type, enclose "boxed" heads or features, and serve numerous other purposes. These line-making devices vary from the finest "hairlines" up to black stripes two or three picas wide. (Fortunately the wide border rules that formerly disfigured many newspaper advertisements are now seldom seen.)

Besides plain, straight rules, there are waved and dotted kinds. There are also parallel rules, with from two to a dozen lines combined on one body. These parallel lines may be all of one weight or combinations of light and dark lines.

Rules for newspaper work, and especially newspaper column rules, usually are made of brass, and may be used for a long time without showing wear.

Slug-casting machines have attachments for making typemetal rules in a great variety of faces. These are limited in length to 5 or 7 inches, that is, to the longest slug any particular machine will produce.

Monotype type casters, however, can be adapted to making rules (or spacing materials), in continuous strips, or in single units. There is also a special strip-making machine, quite generally used, called the Elrod Lead, Slug, Rule, and Base Caster, which offers a large variety of rules and decorative borders.

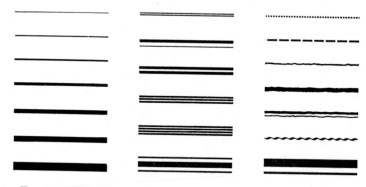

FIG. 30.—A few of the innumerable kinds of printers' rules

Newspapers everywhere use strip casters to provide an abundance of new rules and borders, and also to provide a never-failing supply of leads and slugs.

While the type-metal rules made by any of these machines are not as durable as those made of brass, they have the virtue of being inexpensive. This sort of material is well designed for the uses of advertisers and is widely used for such purposes.

Decorative borders.—Continuous lines of decorative material, more intricate than ruled lines, are called *borders*. These are continuous strips or separate units which must be set in lines as type is set. The student is referred to type catalogues or to the matrix-border sections of type-setting-machine specimen books for showings of borders in great profusion and variety.

Most newspaper borders are cast on strip machines or from *border slides* on slug machines.

FIG. 31.—A dozen varieties of type-cast borders

Corners.—In using strip rules or borders to make boxes, or in any situation where two strips meet at right angles, a special problem arises. Except in relatively few cases, the two pieces cannot be "butted" together. Most borders and rules have shoulders like type, which causes a gap between the corners.

FIG. 32.—Three ways of turning corners with a continuous border; (*left*) with a corner piece; (*center*) simply butted together; (*right*) mitered.

This opening between two strips looks unfinished. The difficulty can be overcome in several ways. The direct way, of course, is to miter the ends just as a carpenter miters wood. Machines are available for the purpose, and this is the usual procedure in commercial shops and in newspaper composing rooms. It is also common practice to cast at the end of one of the rules a small *corner piece,* in some geometrical form, which serves to fill the gap neatly.

Ornaments.—Border units frequently can be used alone in various ways, as *ornaments* or "dingbats." There are numerous other kinds of ornaments for printing use. The type- and matrix-specimen books show many pages of these materials.

FIG. 33.—There are literally thousands of ornaments shown in type-founders' catalogues and elsewhere. The illustration shows a few of them.

Dashes.—The newspaper make-up man is very actively concerned with *dashes*. These are the rules which appear between articles, and the shorter rules which separate the "decks" of traditionally styled heads.

FIG. 34.—Top to bottom: jim dash; thirty dash; cut-off rule; same with cornerpiece (used to "box" stories); and ornamental dash.

These short dashes usually are about three picas wide. They are called variously "3-em dashes," "jim dashes," and, in some parts of this country, "misery dashes." Column-width Linotype or Intertype slugs are used, on which several em dashes of the body font have been cast to make a continuous dash.

Dashes between stories are longer rows of em dashes, although some newspapers use tapered or specially designed rules for this purpose. The usual width is about six picas. These longer dashes are universally called "thirty dashes."

"Streamlined" pages, now widely seen, omit dashes from their flush-left headlines; and some papers even omit dashes between stories or use full-width cut-off rules.

Older papers used a decorative dash to separate editorials. These "editorial dashes" have practically disappeared, but here and there a paper may be found that uses them. The phrase "run it over an editorial dash" is heard occasionally.

News cut-off rules complete the equipment of the make-up man. These are used wherever a column is broken and its matter is carried to the next column, and in other places where stories must be separated distinctly.

Braces, parentheses, brackets.—The distinction between these three terms should be noted. Braces ⏤⏤ enclose or hold together two or more lines. These type elements are made in all lengths and weights of line.

Parentheses ( ) and brackets [ ] enclose explanatory or supplied words or phrases and are made to suit the type with which they are to be used. Most fonts include a supply of parentheses, but brackets—or "square" brackets, as they are frequently called—are extra sorts, and are seldom seen in newspapers.

Special characters.—There is scarcely a written symbol or character used in any trade, science, or other human affair that is not duplicated in type form. A few of these, such as common fractions, contract-bridge symbols, chess and checker symbols, and market-page devices, are seen in newspapers. Most of the great variety of special characters are, however, employed by commercial printers exclusively.

Ligatures and logotypes.—Two or more letters may be joined as one, as æ, œ, etc. These are called *ligatures*. Two or more letters which occur together frequently may be made as one piece of type or as a single matrix. In this case the combination is a *logotype*.

The of

With many type faces, the forward turn of the top of the lower-case *f* brings it into conflict with other ascending letters,

such as *i* or *l*. For this reason most Roman and Italic fonts include five *f*-ligatures:

fi   ff   fl   ffi   ffl   *ffl*   *ffi*   *fl*   *ff*   *fi*

Another whole series of logotypes, many of which are finding their way into well-spaced headlines, are combinations made
up of two capitals, especially italics, and certain upper- and
lower-case combinations:

TA VA WA PA FA Wa We Va Ve Wa We Va Ve

Set without logotypes these would look like this:

TA VA WA PA FA Wa We Va Ve Wa We Va Ve

Whole words are cast sometimes as one type, often with a
decorative flourish. Mailing lists reduce a great amount of information to small compass with compact logotypes of words
used frequently in addresses. Calendars usually are set with
logotypes that make it possible to assemble quickly the heading
and figures for any month and year.

Newspapers use logotypes to identify press services, such
as (*AP*), and as labels for news stories to show their source or to
protect them from infringement of copyrights. A circled © is
a logotype meaning "copyright."

Advertisers' signatures or name slugs are logotypes of store
names or brand trademarks. Departments or daily features in
newspapers are distinguished frequently by some form of logotype heading.

Swash letters.—Many fonts are supplied with looped and
flourished decorative capitals. Italics particularly have such
letters to be used occasionally in place of the regular caps. These
characters are called *swash letters*.

Initial letters.—Among the special characters that are cast
in type molds are *initials*, used at the beginnings of chapters in

books or to start paragraphs. Initials range from plain capital letters to most elaborately designed and decorated ones, usually with the letter and decoration enclosed in a square or oblong frame. Designs generally are conventional, but occasionally an illustration is combined with the initial letter.

The plainer sorts of initials, generally large capitals, are properly used by many newspapers to "dress up" the first paragraphs of editorials or featured stories. It was the practice of early-day American newspapers, as it is of many English papers today, to use a large initial capital to begin each important story, and particularly those on page one.

Fig. 35.—Swash capitals, and decorative initial letters

Slug-composing machines can cast a large capital on the first slug line of a paragraph and allow it to overhang and rest on a blank space on the second slug line. This is sometimes done in classified advertisements. Application of the method to large initials is not advisable. If the letter overhangs more than six or eight points, it is liable to break off in making the stereotype mat. If this occurs, the line must be reset and the page made over, with attendant cost and loss of time.

Spacing materials.—Spaces between words and quads that fill out lines have been described. Other blank-space materials are *leads* and *slugs* and *furniture*. Leads and slugs are used between lines and to separate paragraphs. Leads are the thinner strips—1, 2, 3, or 4 points thick. Slugs range from 5 to 12 points in thickness.

Unless another thickness is specified, a lead is understood to mean a 2-point lead and a slug a 6-point slug. The latter often is called a "nonpareil" or a "nonpareil slug." The name comes from the old nonpareil size of type, which was about 6-point.

Larger blank areas are filled with *furniture*. This may be made of either metal or wood. Wood furniture is used around the outside of a type assembly, next to the iron frame, or *chase*, which surrounds it on the press. Wood furniture is sometimes called "lock-up" furniture, since with its help type is locked up in chases in commercial printing offices.

Metal furniture is used where exactness is required. Made of type metal, iron, or aluminum alloy, it is supplied in all sizes, from 2 by 3 picas up.

All furniture is conformed to pica or half-pica measurements. Wood, of course, is seldom accurate.

CHAPTER SIX

Newspaper Typography

Typographical factors in page make-up; need for
headlines; headline purposes and uses; traditional
headline schedules; character counts; principles
involved in "no-count," flush-left heads; streamlined pages; newspaper body types

HAVE you ever tried to imagine what a newspaper page would
look like without headlines? It wouldn't be a newspaper, for
headlines *make* the newspaper, in more senses than one.

There are many kinds of headlines—many varieties, many
sizes, many typographical treatments. In early newspapers only
the principal stories were preceded by headlines. These took the
form of single, centered lines of capitals. From this simple beginning evolved modern headline schedules, which range from
"one" heads up to eight-column banners, with a bewildering
array of "steplines," "decks," and "barlines."

Newspaper page arrangement, usually called *newspaper
make-up*, combines headlines of various sizes, shapes, and textures with illustrations and text matter to create pleasing and
distinctive page designs. Headlines contribute to the appearance
of pages positively and in two ways: They figure largely in a
certain totality of effect, in what may be called the "character"

of pages; and they help to impart the elementary aesthetic qualities of good typographical design.

A page without headlines would present a dull and monoto-
nous area of gray. To impart the elements of design to pages it
is necessary to supply other elements which differ noticeably
from the gray background. The appearance of a page is determined by the character of these elements and their relative positions in the page. In practice these page elements vary in size,
shape, intensity, and conformation. Make-up is the harmonious
arrangement of these dissimilar elements.

It seems safe to say that every newspaper devotes a large
measure of attention to its make-up. Most papers seek to display a distinctive page make-up, and especially to have distinctive front pages. The whole appearance of the front page is
changed for every issue, and, in the case of metropolitan dailies,
for each edition.

A well-designed type page of any kind possesses the following aesthetic qualities:

balance	*rhythmic organization*
harmony	*coherence*
organic structure	*emphasis*

The degree to which these qualities are imparted to pages de-
pends upon the skill of the one who designs them.

As they apply to the practical considerations of newspaper
make-up, the six aesthetic qualities just listed may be charac-
terized as follows:

Balance is physiological. We feel it. A page that is "out of
balance" will distress everyone who sees it. There are two kinds
of balance, formal and informal. Formal balance places equal
elements at equal distances on both sides of an imaginary central
line. The human figure is a simple example of formal balance.
Informal balance disposes unequal elements according to their

sizes at greater or less distances from an imaginary line, which may or may not be central to the design. Nearly all newspaper pages are examples of informal balance. Modern "flush-left" headlines are balanced informally.

Harmony as it applies to newspaper make-up is expressed mainly in the proper selection of type faces as to their design and their relative sizes. Violent contrasts in headlines are undesirable. It is unwise to mix members of one class of types with those of another class. Sans Serifs, for example, should not be used in the same page with Romans. To make up headline schedules from various members of one type family is always safe.

Organic structure in newspaper pages relates to the way in which their elements are knit together by the design into a well-engineered, visibly supported whole. A good page "holds together." It is built upon a solid base, and each element assumes its position as part of a well-organized structure.

Rhythmic organization supplies a sense of dynamic movement to pages. It may be compared to the structural rhythm of musical compositions. In newspaper pages rhythmic elements carry the eye of the reader strongly along from top to bottom, following imaginary paths which have been supplied by the designer of the page. This typographical rhythm consists in the alternation of the sizes, shapes, positions, and intensities of page elements. Typical simple rhythmic alternations seen in all pages are light-dark, large-small, right-left, vertical-horizontal. Combinations of these add infinite variety and interest.

Coherence in type arrangements is always a matter of the proper distribution of the white space, that is, of the nonprinting areas which surround headlines and other elements of the page. Coherence resembles organic structure, but it applies more nearly to the relationships between single elements and small details of the structure.

Emphasis is of primary importance. In any design one element must dominate. In newspaper pages the dominant element usually is a main banner line or a large headline, frequently augmented by a three- or four-column illustration. Emphasis requires a gradation in headlines, quite independent of the need for indicating the relative importance of stories. There is a saying that "all emphasis is no emphasis." If all heads are large, no head has emphasis. Small headlines are just as necessary to good page make-up as large ones. Large heads gain in emphasis through being placed at the tops of columns. Small headlines secure emphasis through contrast and relative position.

Function and design are largely interdependent. That is to say, a page that is functionally sound will display many desirable aesthetic qualities—it will be pleasing to the eye. Similarly, a page which pleases the eye probably will evidence good functional design.

Conversely, such incoherent and confused pages as those which characterize many tabloids are both functionally and aesthetically bad. (For this reason, we commonly hear readers of these papers declare that "there's never any news in this paper," or "you can't find anything in this paper.")

Practice in page designing.—Make-up is, after all, a practical matter, and skill in making up pages comes only from long practice. Every page differs from every other. News stories, when set in type, are of all sizes, all shapes, and all degrees of importance. Headlines must "fit" the stories as well as supply the elements of design. Several books are available that deal exhaustively with the principles and methods of newspaper make-up. Except in journalism laboratories, unfortunately, opportunities to experiment with actual type matter and real headlines are limited.

For the student, however, the best way to acquire a knowledge of page make-up is to lay out full-scale, practical pages. Sketches of dummy pages, with penciled indications of type matter and roughly lettered headlines, may be extremely helpful in acquiring a feeling for the organization of page elements. Better still is make-up practice with *proofs of actual materials.* For this purpose printed news stories of various lengths, headlines of all sorts and sizes, an illustration or two, and probably a front-page masthead, are clipped from newspapers and pasted on cardboard, and trimmed closely on all sides. These units may then be arranged on a sheet of paper which bears a penciled outline of the page size, to form an unlimited number of practical pages. Made up in this way, pages can be studied for total effect, and details of their arrangement can be criticized fully as effectively from the student's standpoint as if they were actually made up in type. The method has the great advantage, furthermore, of permitting pages to be assembled very quickly, and to be changed instantly.

Headline purposes and uses.—Newspaper headlines may be said to serve two broad purposes in the design of pages: They provide architectural elements of function and structure, and they help to impart aesthetic qualities that satisfy the eye and result in a feeling of pleasure on the part of the reader. Beyond this, they give to a newspaper its distinctive "character."

The visible character of a newspaper is one of its most valuable assets. This totality of appearance renders two important services to the paper: (1) it identifies the newspaper instantly, and independently of its contents; (2) it makes it possible, even for individuals who may be seeing the paper for the first time, to sense its editorial policies and to discern the probable social level of its average reader.

From a functional standpoint—that is, quite apart from all considerations of make-up or typography—headlines serve newspapers in the following ways: They may (1) help to "sell" readers the stories in the paper; (2) establish the relative importance of stories; (3) assist readers to find quickly stories in which they are interested; (4) make it possible to distinguish at a glance one day's paper from another day's, or one edition from another; (5) help to create street sales; (6) departmentalize the news matter or features.

Publishers have long been aware of the importance of headlines, and have been giving more and more attention to this feature of their papers, as well as to their general make-up. Many papers have changed their traditional "dress." This has been accomplished by adopting the so-called "no-count," or "streamlined" headlines. In many cases this has involved a change in type faces used for heads. New type faces have been designed solely for such purposes; these and older faces are being used in the new arrangements.

Consideration will be given later in this chapter to the principles which are employed in the streamlining of newspaper headlines and newspaper make-up. First, however, it will be well to examine the time-tried schedules which have served American newspapers for about half a century.

Traditional headlines.—One outstanding characteristic of traditional headlines is the use of all-capitals in top heads. George Bastian wrote in *Editing the Day's News* (1924):

> There are a few newspapers in the country that do not set their headlines in capitals, but use all upper and lower-case letters. The claim is that this makes for greater readability and attractiveness. The top lines set in capitals, however, have come to be accepted as the standard.

It is interesting to observe that today, less than two decades later, the tide has turned and a majority of our newspapers now appear with all their headlines set in caps and lower case.

Headlines evolved from a simple form—a centered line of capitals, usually the capitals of the body type used. This form of head is now, and probably always will be, the basic one. It may stand alone over a story, or may have a simple two- or three-line subheading under it. A line of capitals is used also as a break between other elements in more complicated headings. In this use it is called a *barline* or a *crossline*, and good style requires that it be a full line.

As headlines grew in importance and increased in size and emphasis, a style evolved in which one or two words, set in very large capitals and centered, with explanatory subheadings, pre-

A.I.A. ELECTS CLEVELANDER

Election of William H o r n e r, Cleveland accountant, as an associate in the American Institute of Accountants is announced by John L. Carey, institute secretary. Horner

U.S. TO BUY APRICOTS

Fruit Will Be Taken for Relief and British

WASHINGTON, July 3—(U.P.)—The Agriculture Department announced today it would support the grower

Fɪɢ. 36.—The simplest form of headline, usually called a "one" head, is shown on the left; a simple head, with subhead, or "deck" added, on the right.

ceded important stories in top-of-column positions. The physical limitations of this style are obvious, and it soon was superseded by two or three lines of capitals, set in steps, and named *stepline*, or *dropline*, heads.

FOOD PLAN

Is Held Up In House

All Stores Will Stay Open
Every Evening Until
Curfew Rings

Fɪɢ. 37.—"Exclamatory" headline, for use at top of column. This forerunner of the multiple-element heading, is still seen occasionally.

Frequently this kind of headline is set with all lines full lines, as in Figure 39 below. In this case the heading is said to be "set flush," and this is so indicated to the printer by the headline writer.

Steplines are used frequently directly over stories, that is, without subheadings. In most cases, however, one or more *decks*, of two, three, or four lines each, and set in caps-and-lower-case type smaller than the main headlines, are used to supplement

CUBS DROP CARDS INTO FIRST PLACE TIE WITH DODGERS

Score 2 Unearned Runs in Fifth Inning to Win for Passeau, 2 to 1

FIG. 38. — Three-line stepline, with pyramid deck.

and explain the top lines. These decks or *banks* may be set as inverted pyramids, or in hanging-indention style, as shown below.

PLANT BOOM IN EAST HITS 1250 MILLIONS

Commerce Chamber Gives Figures for Past Year; 321 Firms Expand

FIG. 39. — "Set-flush" stepline; pyramid deck.

ROOSEVELT SPEAKS FROM HOME TODAY

Extends Hyde Park Stay for Broadcast to Nation; On All Networks at 4 P.M.

FIG. 40.—Stepline with hanging indention deck.

We have, then, these three elementary headline elements: (1) the centered line of capitals; (2) the all-cap stepline top heading;[1] (3) the cap-and-lower-case deck. From these, singly or

[1] Hearst newspapers use all-cap top heads set in pyramid form.

in combination, all traditional headline schedules are made up. Even the *banner* heading of seven- or eight-column width is simply an exaggerated barline. Boxed heads, also, conform usually to one of the standard forms.

Headline schedules have been mentioned. These printed examples of a newspaper's heading styles, which are used by all large newspapers and most small ones, serve several important functions. They restrict to a workable minimum the number and kinds of headlines to be used in the particular newspaper. They show the type faces which are available in the newspaper's composing room, and show them set in practical forms. The editorial staff thus is provided with a definite, easily understood plan for each kind of heading. Again, the headline writer finds in the schedule a complete gradation in size and emphasis. He is thereby enabled to assign to any particular story a headline that establishes its importance in comparison with other stories in the paper.

Most headline schedules provide certain special heads for one or more departments. Sports stories, for example, usually appear under headlines selected from a schedule different from the one used for other stories.

Typographically, newspaper headings present problems of several sorts. Restricting type lines to definite forms imposes very definite limitations upon the wording of such lines. These limitations increase greatly as we reduce the number of letters in a line. In one-column headings, to take a practical example, it has been found that if there are fewer than 14 letters and spaces in each line it is difficult to write heads that will convey intelligible meanings. Types for one-column headlines, if larger than say 18-point, must therefore be *condensed* in design.

MATCHES ARE HEAVILY TAXED | MATCHES ARE NOT TAXED

Fig. 41.—Barline, set in extra-condensed Gothic type. | Fig. 42.—The same, set in a less-condensed face.

An examination of the wording of Figures 41 and 42 will show that the headline writer has been helped by the greater character-count which the condensed type form affords.

There is a typographical ideal for the length of the individual lines of stepline headings. For example, one-column headings look best if each of their lines is approximately 11 picas in width, and if all the lines of any head are nearly equal. (This does not apply, of course, to heads in which all lines are set full measure, such as those of the *New York Herald-Tribune*.)

GIVES UNCLE SAM STRONG PEP TALK

FIG. 43. — A well - constructed stepline.

GIVES UNCLE SAM PEP TALK

FIG. 44.—Poor stepline—second line too short.

GIVES UNCLE PEP TALK

FIG. 45.—Poor stepline—both lines too short

If a headline "says something" in acceptable wording (and students of journalism all know what this means), and is typographically pleasing, it represents a high degree of competence on the part of its writer. Neal says, in *Newspaper Desk Work:*

> When a desk man summarizes a 2,000-word story so well in the thirty-five or forty words of a four-part headline that the reader draws all the essentials of the news from the headline alone, he produces journalistic literature which for compression and power rates AA-1.

To this one may well add that when he accomplishes his task within the rigid mechanical requirements of the traditional headline schedule, he is a master indeed.

The writer of headlines is required to determine with considerable accuracy, and before the actual typesetting is done, how wide each line he writes will be when it is set in a specific size and kind of type. A simple counting of letters is not sufficient. The letters of our alphabet, and especially its capital letters, vary greatly in width. The headline writer must take these differences into account. The following method gives a workable approximation of the width of most headline types:

For headlines set in capitals—
  M, W = 1½ units; I = ½ unit; all others = 1 unit; spaces between words, and punctuation marks = ½ unit

For headlines set in caps and lower-case—
  M, W = 2 units; I = 1 unit; all other capitals = 1½ units; m, w = 1½ units; i, l = ½ unit; all other lower-case letters, and figures = 1 unit; punctuation marks and spaces between words = ½ unit

1-½-1½-1-½-1 - 1-½-1-1-1-½-1-1-½-1 - 1 - 1½ = 15½ units
LIMA STIRS UP ROW

1½-½-1½-1-½ - 2 - ½½½½-1½-1-½-1-½-1½-1-½-1½-1 - 2 = 21 units
Lima Will Stir Up Row

Fɪɢ. 46.—Demonstration of "weighted" letter-counts

For decks set in hanging-indention style and in 8-point or 10-point type, an over-all word-count is usually sufficient. For example, 15 or 16 words will serve for a three-line deck if set in 8-point Cheltenham Bold. For decks above 10-point, however, and for all pyramid decks, it is necessary to count each line accurately. Several decks are shown here to illustrate the need for care in constructing decks.

Supervisors Learn Funds | **Supervisors Told Funds**
Are Running Far Below | **Are Now Below**
Budget Requirements | **Budget Needs**

Fɪɢ. 47.—Good (left) and poor pyramid decks

Supervisors Learn Funds | **Supervisors Learn Funds**
Are Now Much Below | **Are Running Under**
Needs of New Budget | **Budget's Requirements**

FIG. 48.—Good (left) and poor hanging-indention decks

As has been noted, barlines must be full lines. This means that they must be counted.

Two-column headlines are easier to write than one-column, but their typographical requirements are much the same. As headlines increase to three columns and beyond, other mechanical problems arise. The rule is, the larger the head the larger the type size. The "weighted" character-count described above may not be accurate enough for the larger heads. Banner headings, for example, must fit the space allotted to them very accurately. It is usual for some member of the editorial staff to go into the composing room to work out such headings "at the case," with the aid of a compositor.

Aside from the restrictions that good usage has placed upon the actual wording of headlines, good typography and good appearance have dictated certain headline requirements. Some of the more important of these are given below.

Oldstyle Roman faces should not be mixed with Modern Romans, and types which have serifs should not be used in combination with Sans Serifs.

It is desirable to maintain uniformity of "color" in the elements of each heading. Lightface types should not be mixed with bold types.

In cap-and-lower-case heads, each line should start with a capital, even though a word is involved which otherwise would start with a lower-case letter.

There should not be too great a difference in size between a top head and its decks. Ordinarily, 18-point cap heads take 10- or 12-point decks; 24-point heads take 12- or 14-point decks. Very few papers use types larger than 14-point for decks.

Quotation marks make trouble in headlines, because they are too small to "fill out" the ends of lines. When it is necessary to use quotation marks, single quotes are enough.

"Ceiling" for Coal Is Set Up by Officials | 'Ceiling' for Coal Is Set Up by Officials

Fig. 49.—Double "quotes" are undesirable in headlines; (right) single "quotes" look better.

Periods now are omitted from all elements of headlines. It was formerly the custom to place a period after the last word of each deck.

Word-divisions never are permissible in top headlines. In decks, however, it is customary to divide words, just as in the body-matter.

If em-dashes are used in decks, they frequently would fall at the beginnings of lines. This is undesirable from the standpoint of good appearance. For this reason the semicolon is preferred for uses where a comma is insufficient.

Figures are commonly used in headlines to express quantity or number. Rules of printing style which govern the use of figures in straight matter usually do not apply in headings. For example, numbers from one to ten are spelled out in the body of stories, but may be expressed in figures in headlines. It is permissible also to use figures at the beginning of the first line or those of subsequent lines of a head.

Headlines over stories which are indented on both sides should be indented likewise.

Many newspapers which use hanging-indention style for their decks require that the last line of each deck be a full line.

Headline dashes and leading of heads.—The top heads and decks of traditional headlines are separated by short dashes. These usually are plain, straight lines about one-third the width of the column in which they are centered. Some newspapers, however, use special decorative dashes.

Spacing inserted between the type lines of a heading, or above and below the dashes, is called *leading*. Careful attention should be given to the leading of headlines. Figure 50 (below) shows a heading in which the lines, particularly those of the deck, are too crowded; also the dashes are not centered in the spaces they occupy. At the right the lines of the heading have been properly leaded out, and the spacings above and below the dashes have been equalized. The improvement is a decided one.

NEW CONSTRUCTION AWARDS SOAR HERE

U.S. Chamber of Commerce Reports
Highest Net Figures of the
Current Biennium

NEW CONSTRUCTION AWARDS SOAR HERE

U.S. Chamber of Commerce Reports
Highest Net Figures of the
Current Biennium

FIG. 50.—Lines of left-hand are crowded together; they should be leaded out as shown at right.

All headings of the same style should be correctly and *uniformly* leaded.

Leading out of columns.—In making up pages, most columns come out a little short—usually a matter of two or three lines at most. The approved way to lengthen such a column to the uniform page length is to lead out the first few lines of one or more stories. One-point leads should be used for this purpose; two-point leads take less time, but they separate the individual lines too noticeably.

One important rule should be invariably observed—the make-up man, in leading out columns, *never* should change the uniform leading of headings.

"Freak" heads.—All newspapers, and especially those which use so-called "circus make-up," have a few headlines in

their schedules which are employed occasionally to break up the
monotony of pages and to provide a means of accenting unusual
stories. The commonest of these is the boxed heading. The box
may include only the headline, or may enclose headline and

*Must Have Been
At Least Eleven
Other Examples*

FIG. 51.—Typical "boxed" head

story. Other freak styles are the two-column "dingbat" head,
and various italic forms used without decks.

Now Is the Time for All the Good Men

Women Say Dancing Partners Are Few

FIG. 52.—Old-fashioned "dingbat" heading

Type faces used for traditional heads.—Up to the time
of the Spanish-American War, in 1898, single-column headings
were the rule in American newspapers. Even today most stories
in daily papers appear under one-column headlines. This has
largely restricted headline types to condensed faces. Of these
the plain, square letters without terminals, which are known in
the United States as "Gothics," have long predominated.

Typefounders have cut dozens of variations of the Gothic
form, in all weights and all degrees of condensation. Because
most headlines are set in all caps, the founders have cut lower-
case letters for only a few of their Gothics. Figure 53 shows
some of the many kinds of square-line faces to be found in typefounders' catalogues.

Plain HEADLINES **Bold Face** FOR CARD

Fɪɢ. 53.—Some newspaper Gothics: (left to right) Linotype Gothic No. 18; Gothic No. 16; Copperplate Gothic Condensed.

The possibilities of a basic design are illustrated in the three widths of Condensed Gothics shown in Figure 54. All three are

Count Is LESS Few More LETTERS SIMPLE WORDS BEST

Fɪɢ. 54.—An example of relative condensation: Linotype Gothics Nos. 1, 2, and 14.

used for newspaper headlines, but, all things being equal, headline writers have shown a natural preference for the most condensed. It should be observed, however, that too much condensation renders letters illegible, particularly in the smaller sizes.

For more than three decades newspapers have set the greater part of their headlines on line-composing machines. This has tended to restrict the choice of faces for headings. Four type families have, with the Gothics, supplied the requirements of practically all American newspapers. These are the Bodoni, Century, Caslon, and Cheltenham families. In general the members of these families which have seen service as newspaper headlines are Bold, Bold Condensed, Bold Extra Condensed (Title), Bold Italic, Bold Condensed Italic, and, in some in-

Bodoni family is now widely *used for many pur*

Bodoni family is now widely *used for many purposes*

Bodoni family is now widely *used for many purposes*

Bodoni family is now widely used for

Fɪɢ. 55.—Members of the Bodoni family of types are seen in newspapers everywhere today. Shown above, starting at the top: Bodoni Bold and Bold Italic; Bodoni and Italic; Bodoni Book and Italic; Ultra Bodoni—all set in 14-point.

stances, the Light and Medium versions with their Italics. An extra-heavy Bodoni face—Ultra Bodoni and Ultra Bodoni Italic —also is seen frequently. Some newspapers prefer Cloister Bold and Bold Condensed to Caslon Bold and Bold Condensed.

Summary.—Traditional headlines have been evolved from simple one-line centered heads, and are made up of combinations of three basic elements: (1) the all-cap barline; (2) the stepline, usually all caps; and (3) the cap-and-lower-case deck. In writing traditional headlines, great accuracy is necessary to create satisfactory typographical arrangements. Newspaper headline schedules help to maintain uniformity, and to secure precision in the writing of heads. Five type designs only, in various modifications, are used to make practically all the schedules in the United States. These are (1) Gothic, (2) Bodoni, (3) Caslon, (4) Century, and (5) Cheltenham.

Streamlined headlines.—Within the present decade many newspapers have broken away from their traditional headline schedules. We are told that "change for change's sake" is a characteristic of modern industrialized living; but, aside from this universal tendency, there are sound practical reasons and convincing arguments for the redesign of newspaper headlines and the revamping of newspaper typography. Some of these reasons are:

1. Traditional headlines are difficult to write, and their rigid forms often result in absurd and meaningless wordings.

2. Traditional forms are hard to set; it is always necessary to reset many lines for typographical reasons.

3. Traditional headlines are hard to read; all-cap words are less legible than words set in lower case.

4. Traditional headlines enforce traditional make-up, which restricts page layout in many ways.

5. Advertisers, both national and local, employ up-to-the-minute typography, which combines the latest type faces with striking layouts to get effects of freshness and modernity. Ad-

vertising space-buyers view newspapers with eyes that are typographically sophisticated, and these men and women are likely to make their decisions, which are so important to the newspaper owner, on the basis of appearances.

The force of such arguments, and particularly the implications of the last one, are obvious to all alert newspaper managers. They have therefore sought means to modernize the appearance of their pages. To do this has required new page layouts and has involved changes in the presentation of the news itself. Most important of all, however, in imparting a freshness and vigor of presentation are the new headline schedules.

In their search for a practical device for modernizing headlines, newspapers have found that flush-left, cap-and-lower-case headings have many advantages. These are called "no-count" heads because in most cases they do not require careful counting of letters. In their typographical requirements these flush-left headlines permit great flexibility. The first line of a head may be longer or shorter than the succeeding lines; lines may be full width or as short as two-thirds of a column; heads may have two main lines, or three; and any head may run with or without a deck.

American Flyers	Biggest in History
RAF Blasts Hit Rhineland And the Ruhr	**House Group Ready With New Tax Bill**

FIG. 56.—Flush-left headlines from *San Francisco Chronicle*

Headlines of all column-widths follow the same natural pattern, which presents few problems in wording or arrangement, even to the novice headline writer.

It should be noticed that flush-left headlines depend upon an informal or "occult" sense of balance. To illustrate the difference between this and the traditional formal balance, one may think of two types of weighing devices. The apothecaries' bal-

Dr. Gallup Meets Critic With 'Advisory Referendum' Offer

Senator Weer and Others Asked to Help Phrase Questions, to Guard Against Biased Wordings

FIG. 57.—How the *Birmingham* (Ala.) *News* uses streamlined Gothics in streamlined headlines.

ance scale places equal weights at equal distances on each side of a central support. The familiar platform scale uses a small weight comparatively far away from a central support, to balance a greater weight close to the support.

The principle of informal balance is applied when decks are added to flush-left headlines. All lines of the decks are set flush, but the whole deck in each case is indented an appreciable amount from the left side of the column. The smaller types used for decks appear to be less weighty than the larger top lines. Moving them to the right "restores" the balance. Each headline has the appearance of being balanced upon an imaginary point well to the left of the center of the column area it occupies. This balance point varies for each heading, but it is never at the center.

Two simple but fundamental principles apply to headline schedules and to page layouts which employ flush-left heads: (1) the extent of each headline area must be clearly defined; and (2) each headline must be provided with a horizontal, well-defined base.

While column-matter itself is more or less neutral in form, nevertheless it is balanced centrally. This means that, in the new pages, uncentered and centered forms alternate with each other; also that an occasional traditionally centered headline may be introduced with pleasing effect and marked emphasis.

Army Tests Barrage of Light To Hide Objectives From Air

Intense Glare Makes Ground Obscure to Flyers, Experiments Conducted by Engineers Reveal

FIG. 58.—The *Los Angeles Times* believes in plenty of "white space" around its headline decks.

Flush-left headlines require, for the most part, only a rough counting of letters. Nevertheless, even the most casual examination of streamlined pages will show that care and skill must be employed in writing these headings. Figure 59 shows a comparison between two treatments of the same heading.

# F. D. R. Speech Marks Highlight Of Quiet Fourth	# F. D. R. Talks On Independence Of Nation
Nation Pauses to Hear President's Address on American Independence	**Nation Pauses For President's Address**

FIG. 59.—Good (left) and poor (right) handling of one-column flush-left head.

Space occupied by the headlines in a streamlined page usually is a little less than would be required for traditional make-up. Individual heads are set in larger types for flush-left treatments, but heads as a whole have fewer lines and are limited to one deck.

Decks for flush-left headlines.—Some evidence exists that newspaper readers as a class read only the top heads and at most the first deck of the traditional four- or five-part heading. The one deck of a modern headline is written in easy paragraph style, and usually takes the form of a résumé-lead to the story it covers.

As has been stated, flush-left top heads may be run with or without decks. This holds true for headlines of any column-width. The new schedules make use of many two-column heads. If a deck is used in a two-column arrangement, in most cases it extends across both columns. The lead for a story under such a headline looks best if it is set in type a size larger than the body of the story, and across two columns.

If a one-column deck is used with a two-column headline, the deck must appear in the right-hand column under the head and the last line of the head itself should be a full line. This arrangement creates a problem, however, with regard to the left-hand column under the head. Any sort of heavy element here will tip the "scale beam" to the left and will destroy the nice balance of the structure. Practically the only solution is to place in the left-hand position a story with a lightface headline, preferably in a box.

In so-called combination headlines, frequently seen at the top of page one, flush-left banner heads of one or more lines are carried down by means of two or more other flush-left lines of various column-widths. Decks are provided in some cases, and pictures are placed adroitly to secure pleasingly balanced effects. Such structures are not difficult to construct, if the scale-beam principle is borne in mind.

Treatment of subsidiary elements.—In flush-left style, dashes, by-lines, news-service lines, copyright lines, and other similar details may be treated as parts of the headline structure, or as parts of the column-matter.

Some newspapers which use flush-left heads omit headline dashes entirely. (This frequently means that "30"-dashes also are omitted.) A few schedules call for flush-left dashes in heads. These are usually half a column wide. Other newspapers center their headline dashes, and still others employ full-width light rules above and below the decks of each headline and between stories. In each of these styles the effect may be pleasing if it is followed consistently.

"By-lines" frequently are set flush, or nearly so. Sometimes, however, they are set down over the text matter at the top of the opening column of the story. In a few newspapers, by-lines over two-column stories are centered on the two columns. In such cases a liberal amount of "white space" is needed above and below any by-line, since centering an element in flush-left style tends to destroy the informal balance.

Flush-left typography.—The newer schedules make effective use of both lightface and boldface types, usually in families. A headline set entirely in boldface may be placed in a balanced scheme with one or more set entirely in lightface. Similarly, bold and light headings may alternate in a column. This provides the layout man with a valuable typographical device. Alternating elements of this kind impart the quality of rhythm to pages. A rhythmic sequence of elements is forceful and dynamic, in that it compels the eye of the reader to follow a definite pattern or path. No one can doubt the effectiveness of dynamic pages in comparison with rigid, static ones.

Another use of light and bold types is in so-called "two-tone" headlines, with boldface used as an emphatic lead, followed by words in lightface of the same size which complete the thought.

Crime: **S. F. Sailor Kills Girl and Self in Waikiki**

Draft Dodger: Mother Has Officers Jail Her Own Son

FIG. 60.—"Two-tone" headlines from the *San Francisco Chronicle*

Most of the new schedules show a cap-and-lower-case style, with all words capitalized except *a, an*, and *the* and the prepositions and conjunctions of three letters or less. The first letter of each line of the head is capitalized in all cases. A few newspapers, however, use an all-lower-case style in which only the first word of a head or deck is capitalized.

The use of an occasional all-cap line in flush-left headings should be especially noted. Generally speaking, any line of capitals used in a newspaper, most of whose headings are set in caps and lower case, acquires extra emphasis. Some flush-left schedules use single lines of caps as "catch lines." In such cases, the cap line is set in a size noticeably smaller than the main headline and is placed just above it, sometimes with a flush-left dash between the two parts of the head. The cap line serves to characterize or classify the story. It tells the *kind of story*, or connects a news story with one which has appeared previously, or assigns the material to a locale, or departmentalizes it. All together, cap lines serve many useful purposes in the new make-up.

Types for new headings.—Because flush-left heads depend for their design upon the positions and arrangements of their lines, rather than upon the character of the types composing them, many newspapers have been able to construct new schedules with the types they have at hand. For more than twenty-five

JUST IN CASE

U. S. embassy guard in Rome reinforced

FIG. 61.—A line of capitals used as a "classifying" top line

years the manufacturers of typesetting machines have taken the lead in the design of usable types. The catalogues of the Mergenthaler Linotype Company, the Intertype Corporation, and the Ludlow Typograph Company show the results.

The older Gothics have to a large degree been replaced by redesigned Sans Serifs. The term "Sans Serif" applies of course to all Gothics; but it now serves specifically to identify the Futura and Kabel designs and their derivatives. Moderately condensed versions of these, and also sloping forms, are to be found in most newspaper offices. Characteristically, Sans Serifs are cut in several weights—in some cases, as many as four or five.

Another recently designed sans-serif headletter of ideal design is the Erbar face, cut in Light and Medium weights of a moderately condensed form.

Radiant and Radiant Bold, designed by Douglas McMurtrie for the Ludlow Company, is another new face that is readable, condensed, and perfectly suited for headline use.

Related to the Sans Serifs are the so-called square-serif types. These are based upon older forms. In their various designs and weights, and particularly in moderately condensed versions, the Square Serifs make excellent headlines.

Sans Serifs lend themselves admirably to the spirit of flush-left headings. They provide sharply contrasting versions of uniform designs with which the layout man may create highly desirable page rhythms. They are also well adapted to use in "two-tone" heads. For departmental heads and for accents of various kinds, the sloping versions of sans-serif designs are ideal.

Not all of the new schedules are constructed from Sans Serifs, however. The old stand-bys—Bodoni, Caslon, Century, Cloister, and Cheltenham—when used in the new ways are just as effective as they ever were.

Bodoni particularly is widely used in streamlined pages. The layout man finds ready to his hand the regular Bodoni, and Bodoni Bold, and Ultra Bodoni, each with its Italic; and if he needs a lightface line or two, the Bodoni Book or its Italic.

Summary.—Modern streamlined newspapers make use of "no-count," flush-left, cap-and-lower-case headlines, arranged in informally balanced layouts. The advantages gained are: (1) these heads are easier to write; (2) they are easier to set; (3) they are easier to read; (4) the new effects are dynamic; and (5) advertisers prefer them.

Most flush-left lines are set in cap-and-lower-case style; some newspapers, however, capitalize only the first words of top lines and decks. All-cap "catch lines" are used occasionally to give secondary emphasis.

A column of newspaper body text has the appearance of being centered optically. This helps to produce a sense of relative balance in the out-of-center, flush-left headlines. An occasional centered heading or other element therefore is permissible.

Dashes between the elements of the new headlines may be flush-left—centered—or omitted entirely. By-lines, etc., usually are set flush; but these and other supplementary lines may be centered if desired.

Combinations of lightface and boldface types are used in modern headline schedules to help to impart a dynamic sense of rhythm to pages.

The newer sans-serif types, and particularly those which have been designed especially for headletter uses, are preferred in many new headline schedules. However, older type designs are equally suitable for these purposes and are being widely used.

Newspaper body types.—Much has been printed about the need which modern newspaper production methods have disclosed for improvements in the design of body types. The older faces, of which Modern Roman No. 2 is an example, have proved unsuitable for making good stereotype plates. These types also tend to fill up with ink when they are printed on modern high-speed presses, and especially when presses are equipped with hard-rubber rollers instead of the older resilient ones.

For these reasons the typesetting-machine manufacturers, led by the Mergenthaler Linotype Company, have employed expert designers to modify existing body-type designs so as to provide a number of new faces, each ideally suited to a specific use.

These redesigned types have been shown by tests to be greatly more legible than the older newspaper faces which they replace. While part of this increase in legibility is due to individual letters having been made larger, the amount of space any given story will occupy has been increased very little, if at all, and in some cases this space actually has been decreased. The table below shows the comparative character-counts for Modern Roman No. 2 and several of the redesigned faces:

CHARACTERS TO THE COLUMN-INCH

Name of Type	6 pt.	6½ pt.	6¾ pt.	7 pt.	7½ pt.	8 pt.
Modern Roman No. 2	450	...	...	360	...	297
Excelsior No. 2	450	...	...	360	318	288
Opticon	444	...	...	350	307	279
Paragon	442	...	...	350	307	279
Textype	468	...	...	382	...	315
Ionic	456	410	400	360	322	288
Ideal	468	410	395	360	336	306
Regal No. 1	468	...	...	371	...	306
Regal No. 2	444	...	...	360	...	297
Rex	493	...	...	412	346	324

The nature of the redesigning is indicated in the enlarged specimen letters shown in Figure 62. The "ink traps" in such

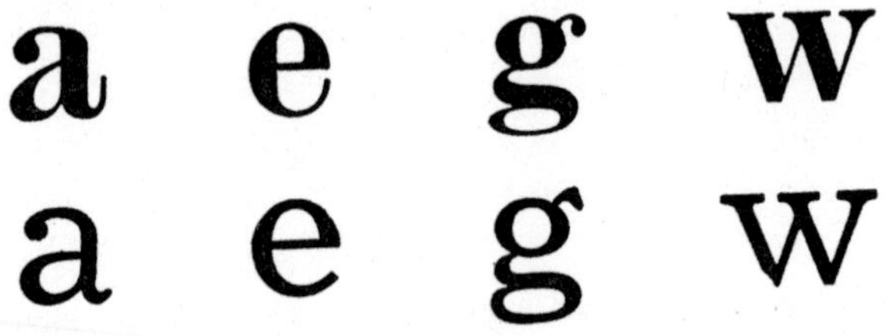

a e g w
a e g w

Fig. 62.—Enlargements of old and new newspaper body types: (*above*) Modern Roman No. 2; (*below*) Mergenthaler Excelsior. Note the absence of "ink traps" in the redesigned face.

letters as *a*, *b*, *e*, *g*, etc., have been opened up. Fitting of the letters is closer, and descending strokes have been shortened.

The new faces are crisp-looking, and they add greatly to the pleasing character of modern newspaper pages.

CHAPTER SEVEN

The Newspaper Composing Room

Kind of press equipment determines procedures; metropolitan newspapers; four departments; how advertising and news copy is handled; smaller newspapers print directly from type

MANY unusual terms and strange names for machines and processes may be heard in newspaper composing rooms. Definitions and explanations for some of these are given in this chapter.

At the outset it should be clearly understood that there are two great classes of newspapers, those which are printed from curved plates, and those which are printed directly from the types themselves. Metropolitan newspapers, requiring large runs, use high-speed rotary presses and stereotype their pages. Their larger composing rooms need a more intricate type of organization, also, than the composing rooms of smaller newspapers. The latter use so-called flat-bed presses, upon the beds of which the type forms are locked. With fewer pages, smaller press runs, and fewer editions, the smaller dailies and the weekly papers require fewer employees and their composing rooms employ much simpler methods.

Let us go first, then, into the composing room of a metropolitan newspaper. Here we shall find the most complete types of organization and methods.

The slip board.—Perhaps the first thing a visitor sees is the *slip board*. This is a wooden or metal bulletin board with grooves for holding narrow "slips" of cardboard, on each of which appears the written or printed name of a regular employee or of a substitute.

It is the universal practice for each newspaper to employ a certain minimum force of men regularly. If pressure of work makes it necessary to employ more men temporarily, these are notified of their employment by the foreman's placing a slip opposite their names on the slip board. This slip reads "Office," and specifies the day and working shift for which each "sub" is thereby hired.

Under union rules no one may work more than a certain number of days or a certain total of hours in any one week. In most cases, when a "regular" does not work he is expected to provide an acceptable substitute. He hires a "sub" from the slip board by "slipping him up." To do this he places a slip bearing his own name opposite the name of the sub, specifying day and shift.

If a sub wishes to lay off, he *turns his slip* face to the board. To quit, he *pulls his slip*. If the foreman pulls a sub's slip, however, he is discharged. A much-coveted slip bears two letters only, *tf*; the fortunate sub who finds it opposite his name is employed regularly until further notice—*"till forbid."*

Four departments.—The composing room has four major departments: the *ad alley* or ad room; the *news side* or machine-composition department; the *proofroom*; and the *make-up department*.

Except for the proofroom, all departments are usually accommodated in one large room without partitions. The equipment itself and its arrangement indicate the imaginary divisions into departments.

The ad alley.—The ad alley is really a big composing room in itself, occasionally occupying a separate floor. It has its own composing machines and numerous cabinets filled with cases of type.

Formerly type cases were kept in open racks, called *frames,* and this word has been carried down to designate the sloping tops of the cabinets. Each workman is assigned one of these top spaces. That is his frame. On it he assembles advertisements in a "job" galley.

To avoid difficulties of handling, page ads are assembled directly in the page truck they are to occupy.

Several kinds of typesetting machines are found in the ad room. Linotypes or Intertypes of the ordinary sort set the body matter for advertisements. Other keyboard-operated Linotypes or Intertypes set the small and medium-sized display lines. Matrices of larger types are set by hand and cast as slugs on the Ludlow Typograph or the All-Purpose Linotype (descriptions of which will be found in chapter eight).

Besides the composing machines, many newspapers use Monotypes or Thompson typecasters to make type for their cases. Strip-material machines, such as the Elrod Lead and Rule Caster, or Monotype casters, especially designed to make strip rules and strip spacing materials, also are standard newspaper equipment.

Inasmuch as all or nearly all the materials and type in their pages are cast by their own machines, a large number of newspapers dump their pages instead of returning the materials to cases. Everything is returned to the metal pots. Under newspaper conditions a considerable saving is effected by this method.

Metal-cutting saws are used for sawing type slugs to length and for cutting metal rules or strip materials. These saws are found universally in composing rooms.

Hand cutters, called lead cutters, which the saws have replaced, still are available for an infrequent line or two, and *mitering machines* are provided for cutting rules at any angle.

Advertising procedures.—Copy for advertisements comes to the ad alley in the form of typewritten sheets accompanied by a *dummy* or *layout.* The *cuts*—engravings—from which the illustrations are reproduced, usually are supplied with the copy. Cuts often are furnished in the form of stereotype matrices. (See page 141.)

The first step in setting an advertisement is to *mark up* the copy for the typesetting machines. Kind of type, size of type, and measure—that is, length of line—are indicated on the copy for each line to be set. Any line that is to be set by hand is marked for size and kind of type and "ringed through" with a pencil-drawn circle.

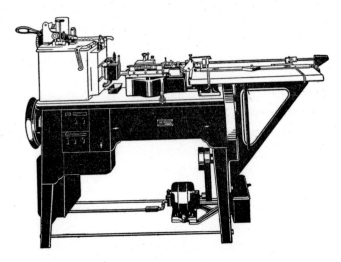

Fig. 63.—Elrod Lead, Slug, Rule, and Base Caster. This machine casts automatically continuous strips of the materials named.

After the machine type has been set, an ad man assembles the various elements according to the layout. Next a proof is pulled, and read by the proofreader. After correction, another proof is pulled, revised, and sent to the advertiser.

After this *author's proof* has been returned with the author's corrections (more often called "author's alterations"), the type is passed along to the make-up department and placed in its specified page, usually in a predetermined position in the page.

A new method of preparing advertisements now is used quite generally by department stores: The advertising department of the store employs artists to draw the illustrations of the merchandise to be advertised. Then proofs of type lines, set either by the newspaper or by outside composing rooms, are pasted on the drawings to make the finished copy. From this, an engraving is made and placed in the newspaper page. This method not only saves time in the composing room of the newspaper, but it makes possible many pleasing typographical effects. The artist can work type lines into illustrations, add shadings over type areas, and employ a number of other effective devices.

On most newspapers advertising deadlines are advanced enough so that nearly all advertisements are set, corrected, OK'd, and in their positions before work starts on the news columns.

The news machines.—The machine-composition department of a newspaper is usually located close to the editorial department. Linotype or Intertype machines—several dozens of them on large papers—are grouped as close together as effective operation will permit.

These machines serve three functions: the setting of news (*straight matter*); the setting of heads; and the setting of classified advertising and market data. On large newspapers these various functions are carried on by different machines. Smaller papers combine them on fewer machines.

In chapter eight various kinds of specialty machines are described. Many of these set large-type headings and display lines for advertisements. Modern line-casting machines can produce practically every line of type used in newspapers.

Operators on news machines receive their copy in *takes*. A take may be one story, a portion of a story, or a number of short items. During the early part of a shift, each take will be about enough type to fill the machine "stick"—ten column-inches. Near an edition closing-time the takes get shorter, down to a paragraph or two, and each story is set on several machines.

Takes are numbered on the copy so that they may be assembled in correct order.

All copy is placed in takes on a spike, or *hook*, beside the *copy-cutter*. This individual is an employee of the composing room, and generally is considered the composing-room foreman's right-hand man. He receives the copy from the editorial department, separates it, and routes heads and other special matter to appropriate machines. News matter, classified, markets, and stocks he sends to machines which set straight matter.

The word *hook* is used in a variety of ways, even when a box takes its place. Copy to be set immediately goes on the *live hook;* filler, good at any time, goes on the *time hook.* After copy has been set it is said to go (or to be) on the *dead hook.* To *work the hook* means to soldier or to shirk work, especially by hunting through the hook for the easiest take.

In passing, it may be noticed that dead copy is usually saved in the newspaper's proofroom for a reasonable time before it is destroyed. This makes it possible to fix responsibility in cases where necessity arises.

The bank.—Conveniently situated with respect to the news machines are a number of grooved-top tables on which narrow galleys are placed. These constitute the *bank* or, as it is called impartially, the *battery,* or *dump.* Each bank has a sloping rack at the rear, to hold various slug accessories. Surplus galleys usually are stored under the bank.

When an operator has completed his take, or when his machine stick is full, he "dumps" it into a galley on the bank. Above the type he has set he places a *take slug* bearing a large-type number which identifies his work on the proof.

The *bank man,* or *battery man,* assembles the heads as they come from the various head machines. He, or one of his assistants, sets any hand-set lines. Then, as the straight matter comes from the machines, the heads are placed over their respective stories before proofs are pulled and sent to the proofroom.

The proofreading department.—Operators may "cuss" *proofreaders* and call their work "comma chasing," but the fact is that the proofroom is indispensable.

The work of proofreading includes the detection and mark- ing of wrong letters, of inconsistencies of style, and of errors in capitalization, punctuation, and spelling. In addition to this, proofreaders also are often expected to check the accuracy of statements and of matters of fact, and to co-operate with the edi- torial copy desk, which is constantly alert to detect libelous state- ments and transgressions of editorial policy. Facts and figures also are checked at the copy desk, but errors frequently "get by" the copyreaders. The proofroom, while it deals largely with mechanical and technical errors and inconsistencies in style, "catches" errors of many sorts.

For example, reporters are not always careful about the spelling of names. To misspell a man's name may offend him seriously. The proofroom often saves the newspapers from egregious errors in this and other matters of fact.

Each proofreader is supplied with a *copyholder*, who reads aloud from the copy or follows it carefully while the proofreader reads aloud from the proof. The duties of the copyholder call for accuracy and close attention to details.

After the proofs are read, they are returned to the machines for correction. After the corrected slugs are inserted, revises are checked by the proofroom before the galleys are taken to the make-up department.

The make-up room.—Where stereotyping is employed, newspaper pages are made up on rolling trucks, sometimes called *turtles*. There is usually a truck for each page. The trucks are made strongly, with heavy iron tops and two-wheel casters at each of the four corners.

On each truck a *chase* is placed. For stereotyping purposes this is a strong steel type-high frame, provided with movable, type-high, steel locking bars at the side and bottom. Heavy machine screws, activated by a powerful wrench, force these bars against the type page to lock up the form.

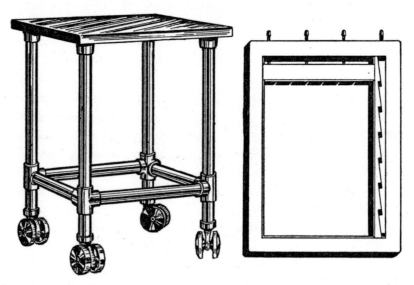

FIG. 64.—Form truck and the chase used for locking up pages that are to be stereotyped.

This term *form* is variously used in a composing room. It is used in nearly every operation associated with page make-up. A form may be an empty chase, or one partially filled with type, or one locked or ready to lock. The foreman tells a compositor to place an advertisement, or directs a galley boy to *dump* a galley of type, *in the form.* When a newspaper has gone to press the *forms are closed.*

After a page is complete it must be justified, by making all the columns the same length. This is accomplished by inserting leads at various appropriate places in the columns until each fits snugly against the bottom bar.

The justified form is then *locked up,* after being *planed down* with a mallet and wooden planer. It is then rolled to the stereo-typing department.

After the necessary number of mats of a form have been made, the form is returned on its truck to the make-up alley.

Some pages run through all editions and are made up but once. Others are made over for each edition. In today's rapid newspaper tempo, with papers in many cities that issue editions almost hourly throughout 24-hour days, the process of production is one of continuous makeover.

Make-up tools.—In handling type and in justifying forms a make-up man uses a specially designed steel rule called a *make-up rule*. This is a relic of hand-setting. It is often called a "hump-backed" rule, from its shape (see Figure 19, p. 47).

Hand compositors and make-up men, as well as most machine operators, keep a graduated brass or wooden measuring gauge always at hand. This is called a *line gauge*. It is usually marked off in three scales of measurement—inches, picas, and agate lines.

Newspapers that use flat-bed presses.—More than 90 per cent of the newspapers of the United States are printed directly from type. These include the smaller dailies and the weeklies. The presses they use are of two kinds. The smallest papers use drum or two-revolution cylinder presses. Sheets of paper are fed through these presses twice, once for each side. Larger circulations demand faster production, and for this purpose flat-bed newspaper perfecting presses are used. These machines, using paper from rolls, print it on both sides, assemble, fold and deliver complete papers.

The composing-room machines and equipment of the smaller newspapers differ from those of the metropolitan papers only in degree. Much that has been stated about organization and methods of operation applies to a large number of smaller dailies and, to some extent, to weeklies.

Forms usually are made up on strong, flat-topped tables having marble or iron surfaces. Form trucks are seldom to be found in smaller composing rooms.

The chases used for the pages are less than type-high. The perfecting type of press employs narrow-margin chases, which are locked up with special devices. Cylinder-press forms are locked up, with one, two, or even four pages in a chase. Sliding metal wedges, called *quoins,* operated with *quoin keys,* are used to apply the necessary pressure to the type matter.

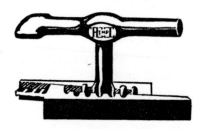

FIG. 65.—Hempel-style quoins, and quoin key

Inasmuch as the type pages must be lifted, in their chases, off from the stones and on to the press bed, justification of the type matter must be done very carefully.

Those newspapers which use cylinder presses not only must run each sheet twice through the press but also must fold the completed papers as a separate operation. Folding machines are used for this, which deliver the folded papers at the rate of two thousand or more an hour. The weeklies usually print one side of the sheet a day or more in advance of publication day.

Pulling proofs.—Whenever proofs are pulled in the composing room, a *brayer* and an *ink slab* are brought into use. The former is illustrated in Figure 29 (page 58). Ink is transferred to the slab with an ink knife and rolled out evenly with the brayer before it is applied to the type. Care must be taken to see that not too much ink is used, or proofs will be smudgy.

On printing presses this same care not to overdo the inking must be observed. Two words are frequently heard in this connection: If surplus ink is used, it may transfer itself from one sheet to the next one in the pile; this is called *offset.* If ink transfers from a too-freshly printed sheet to the press cylinder blanket and thence is retransferred to another sheet in printing, the effect is called *backset*.

Composing-room addenda.—In breaking up dead forms, machine-set matter is dumped, of course, for remelting. Hand-set type usually is distributed, although where type casters are used the whole form may be dumped and nothing saved but the brass rules. Hand-set matter for distribution is placed on the *dead bank*.

Various kinds of type lines may be saved and used several times. These are called *standing matter*. A curious word is loosely applied to standing matter and also to any open, easily set straight matter; the word is *phat*, used also figuratively to mean any easy way or short cut.

Another word of many meanings is *slug*. It may be either noun, adjective, or verb. Any line of type that comes from a Linotype, Intertype, or Ludlow is called a slug. These machines are called slug machines. A 6-point blank strip is called a nonpareil slug, or just a slug. To space type widely between lines is to *slug out*. Then we have *take slugs*, and *galley slugs*, with which galleys are numbered in sequence. *Foot slugs* are used at the bottoms of columns.

CHAPTER EIGHT

Machine Composition

Typesetting and type-composing machines; the Mergenthaler Linotype; the Intertype; the Lanston Monotype; the Ludlow Typograph and the All-Purpose Linotype; costs of machine composition

THE history of early attempts to devise a machine to set type is in many ways like that of early attempts to fly. Hundreds of inventors were at work on the problem for more than a century before a really practicable device appeared.

Most of these experimenters sought a machine that would do the work of a hand compositor—set type, justify it in lines, and subsequently distribute it. Curiously enough, it was not the setting that defied mechanical solution, but the justifying and distributing.

The ultimate solution was really quite simple. All machines in use today *make* type. This means they do not have to bother with distributing devices. The used type is simply melted up. Justification is effected by *making spaces* of the required widths. With these two principles established, the invention of practical machines involved only mechanical details.

It may be interesting to know that two machines were invented that solved the problem on its original basis. They provided means for assembling, justifying, and distributing foun-

dry type. These were the Thorne, or Unitype, or Simplex Type-
setter, as the machine was variously called, and the Paige
Compositor.

Setting the type was easy. This needed only a magazine to
hold the different letters in separate channels, with a keyboard-
operated device to eject the selected letters, and an assembling
mechanism to bring them out in an ordered line.

In the Paige, justification was an intricate automatic device
involving a calculating mechanism. In the Thorne, this part of
the process was done by hand; the types came out in a long
line, normally spaced, and the operator or an assistant broke
this line into sections of the required width and justified them
in exactly the same fashion that a hand compositor does.

Both machines used specially made type, with nicks that
served to direct letters automatically into their proper magazine
channels.

Only two of the Paige machines were built. One was erected
in the plant of the *Chicago Tribune;* the other went to the *New
York World.* Further production and use of the device was effectively prevented by the fact that only the inventor and his assistant could operate its tremendously intricate mechanisms.

The Linotype and the Intertype.—The machine which
revolutionized the business of typesetting is the Linotype, invented by Ottmar Mergenthaler. His first machines were marketed in 1887. By 1900, more than seven thousand of them were
in use. Today there is hardly a hamlet in this country without
a Linotype. In foreign countries, too, this machine is to be
found everywhere.

Year by year the Mergenthaler Linotype Company has improved its machines and increased their range of usefulness until
there is scarcely a typesetting purpose to which they are not
adapted. While the Linotype has thus been enormously improved from the crude models of the 'nineties, its essential parts
have not been changed.

A competing machine, the Intertype, was placed on the market in 1912, after certain Mergenthaler patents had expired. In its operations this machine differs only in mechanical detail from the parent Linotype.

These machines are simple in action. A magazine is provided for holding brass matrices. A keyboard-operated mechanism ejects these "mats" into an assembler. Spaces are provided for by two-part steel wedges, *spacebands*.

When a line of mats and spacebands is full, or nearly so, it moves to a position before a metal mold cell, of which the matrices then form one side. At this point and before the casting takes place, the wedge-like spacebands are driven up to justify the line, that is, to spread it to its required length.

Next a plunger forces molten metal into the mold, where it cools instantly. Thus there is formed a single, type-high line or slug bearing characters formed by the matrices. This slug is automatically trimmed and ejected into the stick.

One more operation is necessary. The matrices must be returned to their places in the magazine. They are lifted to the top of the machine and transferred to a V-shaped, grooved bar. Here the "ears" of the matrices are engaged in the square threads of a revolving worm that extends the full width of the magazine and serves to move them across the upper, open end of the magazine. Each matrix has a V-slot, with from one to seven teeth on each side of the V. By these teeth the matrix is suspended from the grooved bar. The grooves in the bar are not continuous, but are arranged to terminate progressively so as to release individual matrices as the tooth-combinations determine. When a mat is thus released, it drops directly into its own channel in the magazine.

The first Linotypes had only one narrow magazine and one mold of mixed size, and each matrix bore one character. Today's machines have as many as eight magazines, any of which may easily be brought into use, all interchangeable or replace-

FIG. 66.—
Mergenthaler
Linotype

FIG. 67.—
"Streamlined"
Intertype

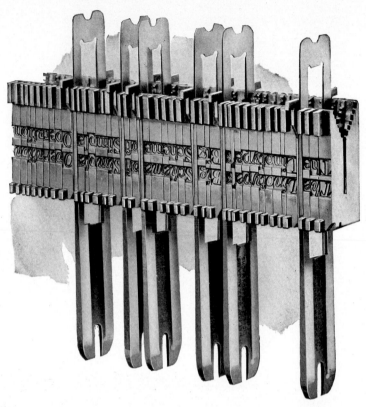

FIG. 68.—Casting side of a line of Linotype matrices, with spacebands. These are two-letter matrices, Roman and Italic.

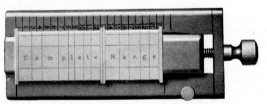

FIG. 70.—Composing stick used with Ludlow Typograph.

FIG. 69.—Linotype one-letter matrix, used for head-line and display composition.

FIG. 71.—Matrices for Ludlow Typograph.

able by others. Not only this, but most matrices have two characters impressed in them, either of which can be brought into
position over the mold. Moreover, practically all modern machines carry at least four or as many as six adjustable molds in
a revolving disk, any one of which can be turned into position
in an instant. The operator of one of these machines therefore
is able to produce as many as twelve different kinds of type
without leaving his chair. This feature of flexibility and quick
change from one type face to another has made Linotypes and
Intertypes practical and economical even for small newspapers
and for commercial shops having need for only a single machine.

For many years the largest type size the Linotype would
accommodate was 14-point. Then so-called headletter molds
were developed which produce cored-out slugs as large as 45-
point. In 1935 a new display Linotype appeared which casts a
45-point slug 42 picas long.

Until recently the narrow magazine channels of the slug-composing machines have prevented the use of any but very condensed faces in the larger sizes. Now, special wide-channel
magazines, and so-called "side" (auxiliary) magazines, have
increased the range of the larger faces. Both Linotype and Intertype offer models with various combinations of 55-channel,
72-channel, and the standard 90-channel kinds. The Linotype
also has a model with extra wide magazines. By means of these
it is possible to compose from the keyboard, assemble, cast, and
distribute automatically, full-width faces such as Bodoni Bold
in sizes up to 36-point. Even "normal" 42-point faces of some
fonts will run without difficulty in the latest machines.

Modern molds are adjustable for both length and thickness.
For a long time 30 picas was the extreme line width possible, but
machines equipped with 36-pica and 42-pica molds are now
available.

Metal pots, formerly heated by gas, now are electrically
heated almost universally. Improved thermostats for electric

metal pots make possible close control of the temperature of the molten metal. This is highly important in the casting of satisfactory slugs.

Most newspaper machines are provided with metal-feeding devices which automatically provide fresh supplies of metal as the production of slugs lowers the amount of molten material in the metal pots.

The Monotype.—There is another and an entirely different type-composing machine called the *Lanston Monotype*. This machine casts and composes separate, *individual* types. It can be used to cast types for the case to be hand-set like foundry types, or it will produce single types in justified lines. In the latter instance the operations of *keyboarding* the copy and of *casting* the types are performed on different machines.

Except that it has many more rows of keys, the Monotype keyboard resembles a large-size typewriter. Pressing a key perforates holes in a paper tape, each character being represented by a different set of perforations. The tape thus prepared is run through the casting device, or *caster*. Here the various combinations of perforations operate stops which control the movements of a *matrix case*. This latter device is only three inches square, yet each one of these cases contains separate matrices for 225 type characters of 12-point size or smaller.

The matrix case is moved automatically by the tape perforations to bring into position over a variable mold any character selected. Then a plunger descends to cast a single type, which is then ejected into its place in the stick. The mold moves again, and the next letter is cast, and so on. Naturally the movements of the mold and the operations of casting and ejecting are made very rapidly.

Justification of Monotype lines, always a major problem in typesetting, is handled by a rather complex device. When the keyboard operator reaches the end of a line, the machine indicates the amount of space which must be placed between words to justify the line, that is, to bring it to the exact width of the rest of the lines. The operator then strikes the appropriate keys to indicate to the casting mechanism what width spaces to make

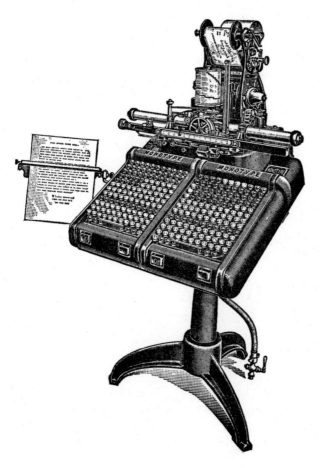

FIG. 72.—Monotype keyboard

for this particular line. As the tape is run through the caster backwards, the combination for the proper size spaces for each line is set before the line is cast.

Not used for news matter.—While it would be perfectly possible for newspapers to set straight matter on Monotype machines, practically no newspapers do so. This is principally

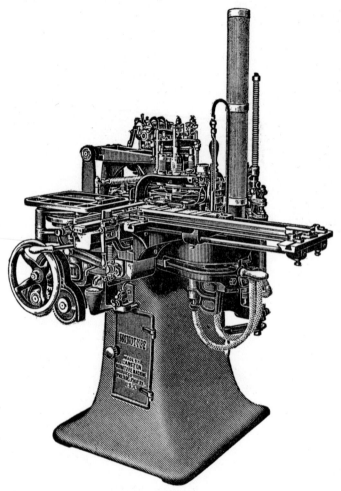

Fig. 73.—Monotype caster. This machine casts and sets types in justified lines.

because composition made up of single types, no matter how produced, must be handled with very much greater care than slugs, the letters of which cannot be pied. Monotype composition is used widely for fine books.

The Monotype machine comes into its own when setting all kinds of intricate tables, particularly when columns are to be separated by vertical rules. The thickness of each letter of any Monotype font is a multiple of a basic unit. This unit is one-eighteenth of the em-quad of the type size involved. These units, as has been stated, are computed by the machine as the individual letters are keyboarded. By means of an indicating device, the operator can establish in a line any number of accurately spaced intermediate columns. Strip rules then can be inserted between the single types to separate the individual columns so established.

The ordinary Monotype caster can be equipped to cast case types, or to make strip materials, such as rules or leads and slugs. However, the Monotype machine usually found in newspaper offices is either the so-called Giant Caster, or the Material Maker. Each of these machines makes various kinds of spacing materials, as well as type rules and borders. The Giant Caster also produces case types in sizes up to full 72-point. It also will cast and compose types up to 18-point in justified lines, using larger matrix cases for sizes above 12-point.

Rapid material making.—Both the Giant Caster and the Material Maker will produce continuous strips of leads, slugs, rules, or borders. Or they will cast metal furniture in strips, cored out to reduce weight, in thicknesses of from 18 points up to 72 points. All these materials can be delivered from the machines in strips or in accurately cast lengths of from one pica up to a hundred picas or more.

A valuable feature of Monotype metal furniture is the fact that it may be made in various heights and used as a base for printing plates. The usual heights are "low" (0.759 inch) for electros or stereos, and "high" (0.853 inch) for zincos or copper half-tones.

Another use for these special Monotype casters is in the production of dashes, cut-off rules, and other materials, in accurate sizes, at the rate of 40 to 50 pieces a minute.

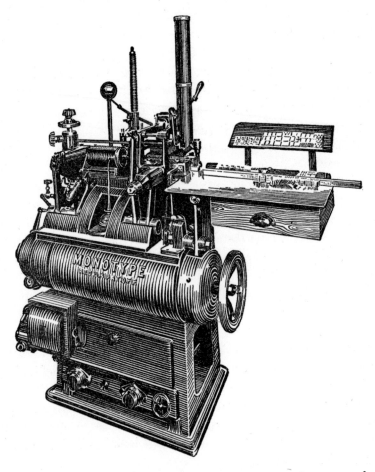

FIG. 74.—Monotype Giant Caster. This machine casts large types for hand composition, and makes strip materials.

The metal used for casting case types on the Monotype may be almost as hard as that used for foundry types. Such metal, however, is not suitable for the machine when it is being used as a composing device.

The Lansing Monotype Company pioneered the whole idea of nondistribution of type forms, and this organization has contrived various units which produce materials so efficiently that their cost when made new is low enough to make distribution unprofitable.

Mixer machines.—For a long time the Monotype was the only machine that permitted "mixing," that is, setting more than two distinct kinds of type in a single line. For this reason the Monotype was and is used largely for setting textbooks and reference works. Dictionaries usually have been composed on this machine.

The Linotype and the Intertype machines formerly were limited to assembling in any one line matrices from one magazine only. While more than one magazine might be available on the machine, the matrices from different magazines could not be mixed. The only combinations possible were either lightface with boldface, or Roman with Italic. If lightface, boldface, *and* Italic were wanted in combination, it was necessary on slug machines to set them separately and then to assemble the small slug units by hand.

Now, however, the slug-composing machines offer so-called *mixer models.* By merely touching a key, the operator of a modern Linotype or Intertype can release into the assembler matrices from two or more magazines. After casting, the machine returns each matrix automatically to its proper magazine.

Manufacturers improve machines.—All composing-machine manufacturers are constantly on the alert for possible improvements of their products.

Some of the recent examples of progress in slug-composing machines are: Automatic devices for centering lines or quadding out blank lines; mold-disks which accommodate six molds; improved mold-cooling devices; light-weight magazines to facilitate changing; low-slug attachments; automatic saws which cut the slugs to length as they leave the mold; faster magazine lifts; and 18-point and 24-point two-letter matrices.

The machine manufacturers have been energetic also in creating new type faces and in adapting for machine use every design that seems likely to become useful or popular. It may truly be said that the designers of types for composing machines are setting the typographical pace for the world.

Slugs versus single types.—The Linotype and the Intertype completely supply the straight-matter needs of the modern newspaper. To a large extent, too, headlines are produced by these machines.

In the book field, also, the slug-composing machines predominate. For example, in the annual competition held in 1940 in the United States to determine the fifty "best" books, 30 machine-set and 20 hand-set books were selected. Of the 30 set by machine, 21 were Linotype or Intertype, and only 9 Monotype. Among "trade" books and popular editions the slug-composed proportion is even higher.

As has been said, all countries use composing machines, mostly Linotypes or Intertypes. Matrices are cut for practically every language, even for Chinese and Sanskrit.

The Ludlow Typograph.—With the Ludlow system of composition, individual matrices are set by hand from a case resembling a type case. A special stick is used which, with its matrices, is inserted into the casting machine to produce a corresponding line of type in slug form. Justification is done by hand in the same way as with foundry types, and the matrices are distributed by hand.

The Ludlow Typograph is not a straight-matter machine but was developed to take care of job and display composition. The mechanical part of the Ludlow is a simple casting device using but one mold for all sizes of type.

Ludlow matrix trays or cases are relatively smaller than type cases, since only a few matrices of each letter are required. A caster with two or three matrix cabinets occupies comparatively little floor space and yet may take the place of several ordinary type cabinets.

When this machine was first advertised, printers said: "If we have to set the mats by hand and distribute them in the same

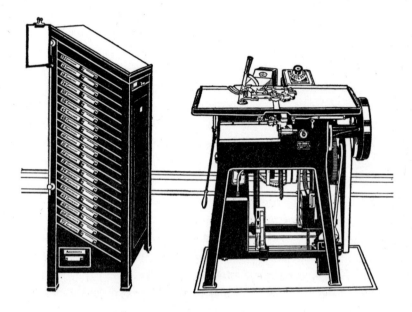

Fig. 75.—Ludlow Typograph (*right*) and matrix cabinet. A stick containing hand-set matrices is used in this machine to cast slug lines.

way as type, we might as well set type." But the several advantages of having a never-failing supply of letters, of always having a new, clean type face to print from, and of handling slug lines instead of lines of single types have brought the Ludlow into general use. It is used in commercial offices as well as in newspaper composing rooms.

The Ludlow has proved to be a remarkably useful and efficient tool for the printer. For one thing, the setting of the matrices is done in a way that is notably faster than setting type in a stick. Tests under normal shop conditions and in many places have demonstrated that Ludlow composition may be done in 25 to 40 per cent less time than case-type composition. This includes the time required to distribute the matrices after each line is cast. If the time necessary to distribute the case types is counted, there is an even greater superiority with the machine.

Special Ludlow sticks, which center lines or quad them out automatically, add to the efficiency of operation.

A special use for the Ludlow is the setting of down-and-cross-rule forms, which can be cast on the machine, using ingenious matrices which make accurately fitting, interlocking rules. Such tabular forms, if set in the usual way with separate rules, are expensive to produce. With the Ludlow, the cost is radically reduced and there is the further opportunity of casting repeat forms, thereby making it possible to cut down press time by printing two or more duplicate forms at once.

The All-Purpose Linotype.—The A-P-L, as it is called, is another machine which, like the Ludlow Typograph, uses matrices set by hand from a case. The machine itself is, in effect, the line-casting part of a Linotype. The matrices are of a special kind and are assembled in a stick and justified by the compositor. Magazine matrices may be used also.

A stickful of matrices, after being justified, is slid into a part of the device corresponding to the first elevator. Casting takes place just as in the Linotype composing machine. The slugs are ejected into a water-cooled pan.

The A-P-L is provided with a working top and a metal-cutting saw. This makes it possible for the compositor to assemble complete type forms at the machine.

Advantages of slug display.—Both of these hand-composing, slug-casting devices, the Ludlow Typograph and the A-P-L, are gaining favor with printers everywhere. Many plants have been installed for complete typesetting and make-up service which use machines entirely and have no foundry types at all. Although investment may be much higher in this case than for foundry-type equipment, the machines save both time and labor in the newspaper composing room, and in commercial offices they are highly efficient for many purposes.

While these two machines perform approximately the same functions, they differ in many details. The Ludlow uses but one mold. This may be changed to cast either a 6-point or a 12-point slug on which the type face formed by the matrices is centered vertically. The matrices are deep-driven, so that a considerable proportion of the total height of the line is formed in the matrix itself. Most Ludlow faces overhang the base slug above and below. The overhanging portion is supported upon blank slugs. This is called *underpinning.*

The A-P-L may be operated in the same way as the Ludlow —using a single mold for all sizes of type, and underpinning the product. The face part of the slug may, however, be placed in any desired relation to the base slug itself—centered to over-hang top and bottom, or flush at either the top or the bottom.

The slugs cast by the Ludlow are of one width only. This is 22½ picas. Matrices for longer lines up to eight columns are set in a long stick and justified as though the whole line were to be cast at once. Stops are inserted near the slug-division points. The stick is then inserted in the machine, and slid forward pro-gressively to cast as many slug sections as are necessary to com-plete the line. Letters overhang from one slug to the next at the point of division.

A-P-L molds cast slugs up to 42 picas long. Longer lines are set in sections and butted together. The A-P-L also will cast slugs up to full 72 points thick, using cored-out molds for this purpose. Type sizes for normal Ludlow faces range from 6-point to 96-point. The A-P-L offers type faces up to 144-point.

Italics on both machines are cast from sloping matrices.

This permits perfectly true rendition of designs which have kerned (overhanging) letters. The A-P-L, in fact, suits the slope of its matrices to the faces involved, and uses three different slopes, with special sticks for each.

Surfacing machines.—When large types are cast on slug-machines of any kind, frequently there is difficulty in securing a smooth face on the letters. This is caused by the fact that a large quantity of metal must be driven through a comparatively small opening in the base of the mold and that, as the metal spreads over the broad, cold inner surfaces of the matrices, it has a tendency to cool with a pitted printing surface which repels ink. To overcome this difficulty, the Ludlow and A-P-L have introduced surfacing machines, consisting of cutters revolving at high speed, which shave off an infinitesimal portion of the type face and leave a good printing surface.

The Intertype hand-composing device. — For setting large types by hand the Intertype offers a modification of the regular typesetting machine, called the Auxiliary Stick Attachment. Standing before the machine the compositor moves a lever which tilts the jaw portion of the first elevator upward and forward to permit insertion of a stick in which regular or special matrices have been set and justified. The casting operation is the same as though a line of matrices had reached the first elevator in the ordinary way. The Intertype Company has cut matrices of many large faces to be used in this way.

Which machine?—Modern composing machines that cast type or its adjuncts may be grouped in four general classes: (1) keyboard-composing, slug-casting machines, including the Mergenthaler Linotype and the Intertype; (2) hand-composition, slug-casting devices, including the Ludlow Typograph, the All-Purpose Linotype, and the Intertype Auxiliary Stick Attachment; (3) single-type casting and composing machines, such as the Lanston Monotype; and (4) various machines which function primarily to make the auxiliary materials the printer uses.

Each class of machines is adapted to a certain field of usefulness. While these fields may overlap to an extent with some devices, there is a fairly well-defined range for any machine in which it is more effective than other machines.

The Linotype and the Intertype are supreme in the field of setting straight text matter for newspapers. In the magazine field and in the general commercial straight-matter field, these machines must share the honors with the Monotype.

For tariff work, tabular, statistical, or other intricate columnar composition, or where matter is subject to many changes or corrections after being set, the Monotype is preferred above other machines.

The machines in the second class above are, of course, principally intended for display-type composition. When there is a wide variety of sizes and kinds of type to be set, with only a few lines of each, one of these devices is the thing to use; and for big types above, say 36-point, these display machines are supreme. The Linotype and the Intertype make composing machines for large types, it is true; but magazine changes are comparatively costly. Therefore keyboard display composition is economical only if there are many lines to be set in each size of type.

As has been said, the Ludlow and the A-P-L have proved to be efficient in commercial shops as well as in newspaper offices.

Costs of machines.—In the typesetting-machine field, costs of equipment usually are stated in terms of the cost of the basic machine plus the various elements of equipment which can be used with or applied to the basic device. Matrices are priced separately, and such things as molds and magazines are considered extras. Electric motors and electric pots, saws, and surfacing devices also are priced separately. For these reasons it is difficult to state the cost of any particular machine except in most general terms. The student, however, can form a general idea of the costs of equipment from the following:

Linotypes and Intertypes cost from about $3,000 to over

$8,000 according to model and the number of magazines on the machine. Molds and magazines to the capacity of the machine are included in the base price; matrices to fill the magazines on the machine usually are included.

The average investment per machine in a large newspaper plant is about $4,200, while in one-machine plants, with many magazines and fonts of matrices, it may average over $10,000.

Ludlow and A-P-L installations always are planned to meet the conditions of the plant where they are placed. An average investment for this reason is hard to state, but $5,000 to $7,000 is not unusual for a single machine.

Costs of Monotype installations are about the same as those for well-equipped slug-machine plants. Specially designed machines—the Monotype Giant Caster, the Monotype Material Making Machine, and the Elrod Lead and Rule Caster—range in cost from $2,500 upward depending upon the cost of the equipment required for the purposes for which they are used.

Costs of machine composition.—No extended study of newspaper costs of composition is possible within the scope of this volume. It is possible, however, to state certain comparisons between the labor costs of hand and machine composition and to set forth some general production standards and average costs.

A hand compositor in days before machines came into use was expected to distribute his own case besides setting type and correcting his product. In an eight-hour day a first-class man would fill his cases and would set and correct about 400 lines of 8-point, 12 picas wide. This would measure up as 8,000 (8-point) ems. At 40 cents a thousand ems, the 1890 rate, he would receive $3.20.

Today the average production of news matter per machine on metropolitan newspapers is about 1,400 corrected lines, or 28,000 ems of 8-point. For this the machine operator is paid on the average $9.50.

The labor cost per line in 1890 was about 0.8 cents; today's cost for machine composition is about 0.65 cents per line. It should be noted, however, that at present hourly rates the cost of hand composition would be at least triple the old figure.

Machine composition of simple straight matter in sizes from 6-point to 14-point ranges in selling price, depending upon local trade conditions, from 80 cents to $1.25 per thousand ems, according to type size.

Selling prices of display lines made by machines are not so easy to state. However, trade composing rooms, which sell their product to printers, charge for Ludlow or A-P-L slugs from 11 cents to 15 cents per line according to conditions, and about the same for average display lines set on Linotypes or Intertypes or for Monotype lines set by hand.

CHAPTER NINE

Presses and Processes

Letterpress, lithography, and intaglio printing
methods and machines; methods used for reproducing illustrations; two processes for duplicating
letterpress forms; rubber plates

THE printing industry employs three methods for placing ink
impressions on paper or other surfaces. These are: *Letterpress*,
the kind of printing everyone knows, which uses a raised, or
relief, surface; *Lithography*, which prints from a flat surface; and
Intaglio, in which the inked areas are below the printing surface.

Letterpress, the historic method.—Gutenberg used a
wine press to obtain printed impressions from his types. In order to convert this for printing purposes, a device for inserting
and removing the type bed under the screw-operated press-ram,
or platen, was added. Remarkably enough, this primitive type
of press, without alteration or improvement, was used for all
printing for nearly three hundred years. About 1800 a toggle
movement replaced the screw, but as late as 1840 hand presses
were the universal rule.

The *Times* (London) introduced a power press about 1810,
but it was a crude device. Not until after the middle of the nineteenth century was there important progress in the design of job
presses, and the modern newspaper press dates from 1885.

FIG. 76.—Three ways of printing (left to right): relief, or raised printing; planographic, or flat-surface lithography; intaglio, or below-the-surface printing.

Modern types of presses.—The simplest printing device is the *platen press*. This is used for small sheets and for special process such as die cutting. The paper is placed by hand or by automatic device in position on a flat platen. The machine then closes, clamshell-like, to bring this into contact with the type form. Commercial printers make use of this type of machine.

Cylinder presses consist of a revolving cylinder upon which the paper is placed and a flat bed upon which the type is supported. The relative movements of these two elements are so controlled that the rotating cylinder brings all parts of the paper progressively into contact with the entire type area.

A simple newspaper press is called a *drum cylinder*. This delivers a printed sheet at each revolution of the cylinder.

Two-revolution cylinder presses are the principal machines used by commercial printers, and a large number of newspapers are equipped with this type of press. The cylinder takes a sheet of paper from the feedboard, revolves once to bring it into printing contact with the type form, then revolves a second time without printing to permit the type bed to return to its original position.

Commercial printers are now equipping their pressrooms with comparatively small automatic cylinder presses, many of which are of the two-revolution type.

Some of the larger two-revolution machines are equipped to print two colors on one side of the sheet at one operation.

Flat-bed perfecting presses are used principally for the production of newspapers whose circulation lies roughly between

5,000 and, say, 15,000. As has been said, these machines "perfect," or complete the newspaper, printing on both sides of a continuous web of paper and delivering complete folded copies. The average press of this type will print an eight-page paper. Others will produce complete papers up to 16 pages.

Rotary perfecting presses are used by metropolitan newspapers for circulation requirements which cannot be met by flat-

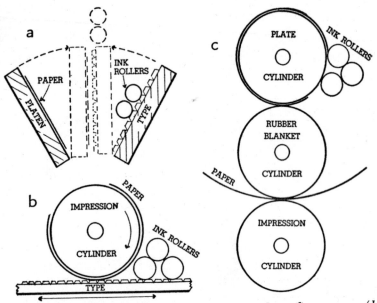

FIG. 77.—Press operating principles: (*a*) platen letterpress; (*b*) cylinder letterpress; (*c*) offset.

bed types. These machines require curved plates, which are produced by the method called stereotyping, which is described on page 140.

These presses are built to fit the requirements of particular newspapers. By combinations of their various units, it is possible to produce newspapers with any (even) number of pages, up to the capacity of the press, and to add one, two, three, or four colors on single pages, or on whole sections. The papers are delivered from the press in sections or in completed form, and at production rates as high as 40,000 per hour.

The factor common to all these machines, and, indeed, the distinguishing characteristic of letterpress itself, is the raised, or relief, surface which conveys the ink to the paper.

The other two processes named at the beginning of this chapter achieve similar results but by different methods. In the printing of illustrations, especially, lithography and intaglio rotogravure are largely employed. But while letterpress may print directly from printer's types, some sort of prepared plate is necessary in all cases for the other processes. Inasmuch as type materials enter largely into the preparation of these plates, much of what has been written in previous chapters is applicable to all three processes.

The following necessarily brief description of lithography and intaglio printing is intended to make clear the relationships of the three basic processes.

Lithography.—This and its derivative processes employ a flat, grained surface on which the design or lettering is established in a medium which repels water. When this surface is rolled, first with water and then with ink, the ink adheres only to the design or lettering. The rest of the wetted areas reject the ink. When the surface then is brought into contact with a sheet of paper, the inked portions faithfully reproduce the original design.

Lithography at first used fine-grained sandstones, but "stone" presses were slow and suitable stones were obtained from only one quarry, in Austria. Then it was found that grained metal plates made of zinc or aluminum could be used in place of the stones. Metal plates have many advantages—they are uniform in structure, light in weight, and easily stored. Moreover, they can be applied to curved cylinders, a fact which makes possible the fast offset presses on which nearly all lithography is done today.

The word *offset* refers to the method of transferring the image from the plate to the paper: The inked and wetted plate prints on a rubber-blanketed cylinder, which in turn "offsets" this ink impression onto the paper, which is held on a third cylinder.

Plates for offset presses bear a printing image in positive form—that is, letters and illustrations appear just as they will on the paper. When transferred to the rubber blanket, this image is reversed, made "negative," like type letters. The transfer to the paper gives a positive image as the final result.

Lithography from stones or metal plates has been used for many years for such diverse purposes as stationery, can labels, and reproductions of paintings in colors. For such work, lithographic surfaces are prepared by tracing on them drawings or portions of drawings, or by transferring, mechanically, proofs of type or of original plates. Hand methods still are used for many purposes.

It was discovered many years ago, however, that photography can be used in platemaking, thereby making hand work unnecessary in many instances, and also making possible many things that hand work cannot effect. This is called *photolithography*, or *photolith* for short.

The process of photolithography starts with a photographic negative of whatever it is desired to reproduce. The copy, or original, may be a drawing or a photograph; it may be a proof of type matter; or it may combine several of these. The original may be reduced, enlarged, or photographed the same size.

Next a grained plate (usually zinc) is coated with a light-sensitive emulsion (consisting of gelatine or albumen with ammonium bichromate in solution), and dried out of contact with light.

This plate is then exposed under the negative to a strong light, just like any photoprint. Where the light reaches the emulsion through the negative, the gelatine (or albumen) is rendered insoluble. After being rolled up with a special ink, the plate is washed with water, which removes the unaffected, soluble portions of the emulsion, leaving the inked, hardened portions in place.

The resulting photographic image on the lithographic plate accepts ink; the rest of the plate rejects it. This is the basis of lithography.

In recent years photolith has assumed a prominent place in the printing world. Small, relatively inexpensive presses and equipment have been placed on the market, and thousands of printers have installed offset departments. There are fields in which a low preparation cost and high speed of production give photolith a very real advantage over letterpress. On the other hand, the process has definite limitations, especially in small plants. Good results depend upon skillful and accurate control of photographic and chemical processes. Ordinarily these skills are not to be found in the small plant.

As a rule, lithography compares unfavorably with letterpress in sharpness of detail and brilliance of color. Here again, high technical skill is necessary to produce plates that will print well.

Variations of the basic lithographic process, such as aquatone and the so-called deep-etch plates, are methods for improving the quality of the product.

To the newspaper owner, photolith so far has offered little. Photo-sections in a few cases have been produced on offset presses, but rotogravure is far superior in quality.

Intaglio processes.—Almost everyone has seen the kind of engraved plates which are used for printing cards. These have the name deep-cut in reverse. To print from such a plate, the pressman passes over it a roller covered with a stiff ink, then wipes the surface of the plate clean with the palm of his hand, leaving the ink only in the incised lines. When he lays a card in place and passes plate and card under a pressure roller, the ink in the lines of the plate "lifts out" and appears, slightly raised, on the surface of the card.

Such is the essence of intaglio printing: Ink is deposited in depressions in a surface; surface ink is removed; and pressure is applied to cause the ink in the depressions to adhere to the paper.

Artists incise or etch drawings on copper to make what are called "plate etchings," such as "dry points." Commercial etchers substitute steel for copper to produce long-lived "steel-die" plates for the sort of letterheadings banks use. These are common examples of intaglio printing. *Photogravure* is a highly technical method for reproducing photographs by intaglio.

The most-used intaglio process is *rotogravure*, the Sunday-supplement picture-section process. Photographs and their type legends are transferred photographically to a copper cylinder or copper sheet. This then is etched in such a way as to leave ink pits of various depths and areas corresponding to the density of the various portions of the illustrations.

In order to print from this copper cylinder it is mounted in a press where it revolves in a bath of very thin ink. As the surface of the cylinder emerges from the bath it is wiped clean by a steel knife, called a "doctor blade." Ink remains only in the depressions in the plate. Next, the cylinder comes into contact with the paper, which, after printing, is carried through heaters to dry the ink, and is then cut up and folded.

Letterpress printing of illustrations.—Even before movable types were invented, wood blocks bearing raised illustrations and lettering were used to print crude books, principally primers for children. These blocks were carved in relief by hand. This process, called *Xylography*, dates from remote times.

The first printers from movable types continued to use woodcuts for illustrations. The art of wood engraving came to its highest perfection during the nineteenth century. Magazines published between 1840 and 1890 show many beautiful woodcut reproductions of drawings and paintings by great artists. At that stage of printing progress, wood engraving was practically the only method available for illustrating letterpress pages.

Intaglio-engraved illustrations also have been used from the earliest days of printing. Copper or steel plates usually are printed on separate sheets, which must at length be inserted or pasted in place.

Today wood engraving is a lost art. Woodcuts were entirely a hand product, which called for artistic ability and skill of a high order. A demand for photomechanical means of reproducing pen drawings was a natural outcome of the growth of printing. The line etching was evolved to supply this demand.

Line etchings, or *zincos*, as they are commonly called, are used universally now to reproduce all illustrations in which black and white are the only contrasts. To make a zinco, a sensitized sheet of zinc is exposed to light under a photographic negative of the copy. The portions of the sensitive coating affected by the light are rendered insoluble in water, and these form a coating which resists the action of an acid bath. After the plate is etched, the protected portions, which constitute the printing surface, appear in relief. Mechanical finishing completes the zinco for relief-printing purposes. Figure 77 is printed from a zinco.

Half-tones.—To reproduce a photograph, either for letterpress or for lithography, it is necessary to provide for innumerable gradations of tone, ranging from pure white through an infinite series of grays to almost solid blacks. For this purpose half-tone plates, or *half-tones*, are produced by photomechanical means.

By the half-tone process a photograph is converted into a pattern of dots the number of which per square inch is the same in all parts of the plate. These dots vary in size according to the intensity of the tone they are to reproduce. In light areas the dots are so small that they almost disappear. At the other ex-

FIG. 78.—Half-tone screens (left to right) : 50-line, 60-line, 65-line, 75-line, 85-line, 100-line

treme—the heavy black areas—the dots join each other to make practically a solid surface.

The dot pattern is produced photographically by means of a glass screen made up of two thin sheets of glass which have been ruled with a diamond point in very fine parallel lines. The two glass sheets are cemented together with the lines of one crossing the lines of the other at right angles. Light transmitted through such a screen is broken up into a series of rays. The intensity of any ray is determined by the amount of light which may reach it through the camera lens.

In practice this screen is placed directly in front of the sensitized plate in the photoengraver's camera. When photographic "copy" is placed before the camera, light is transmitted from its surface, through the screen to the plate. After the plate is developed, the image appears as a multiplicity of tiny dots whose size varies according to the intensity of the rays which have reached the sensitive surface.

The half-tone negative is made into a printing plate in much the same way that zincos are made, except that for fine-screen half-tones copper usually is used in place of zinc.

Under a magnifying glass, the dots of a letterpress half-tone appear as small truncated cones, with the metal between them etched away to a depth of two- to five-thousandths of an inch.

Half-tone screens vary from 25 lines to the inch up to as many as 400 lines. This means that, for the coarsest screen, the number of dots in a square inch will be 25 times 25, or 625. A 400-line screen will have 160,000 dots to the square inch.

Printing the dots of a fine half-tone requires the use of paper with a smooth printing surface. Newspapers use 45-, 55-, and 65-line screens, which give fairly good reproductions, in spite of the fact that the individual dots are visible. Magazines printed on smooth, but uncoated, book papers use, as a rule, 100- or 120-line screens, although 85- and 100-line illustrations are seen occasionally.

Smooth-calendered or coated papers give best results with 133- or 150-line screens. On so-called "double-coated" papers, 175- and 200-line screens are practicable.

Half-tone negatives are used in lithography, just as in letterpress, although the platemaking process is not the same. In photolithography finer screens are practicable on uncoated papers by reason of the fact that the rubber offset blanket conforms itself to any surface.

Process half-tones.—National magazines and many newspapers reproduce natural subjects or paintings in full color. While the technical details of this process are beyond the scope of a brief description, its principles are relatively simple.

The copy for color printing may be an artist's painting, a natural-color photograph, or a color film such as kodachrome. Four half-tone negatives are made, of which three correspond to the primary colors and a fourth, which is printed in black, fulfills the purpose of accentuating the shadows. A half-tone plate is made from each of these negatives. These four plates, after etching, are finished by hand, to secure exact color values.

Filters are used to "separate" the colors. The violet filter used to photograph yellow, for example, absorbs all red or blue light and allows only that light which is reflected by the yellow-content portions of the copy to reach the sensitive film. An orange filter is used for the blue plate, and a green filter for the red plate, while the black plate is photographed through a yellow or amber filter.

Four-color-process half-tone printing is common to both letterpress and lithography, and rotogravure color methods are similar in nature.

The word *register* should be noted in connection with the printing of color plates. Examination of an accurately registered process illustration under a strong magnifying glass will show the importance of placing each colored dot in exact relationship with those which adjoin it. Each group of four dots

—yellow, red, black, and blue—is arranged in a starlike pattern. The eye of the beholder blends light rays from adjacent dots into tones, just as though the colors were blended on an artist's palette.

The allowable variation in the register of the plates of a color reproduction is less than one ten-thousandth of an inch. It is indeed remarkable that ponderous presses, operating at high speeds, are able to achieve such accuracy of register, and to maintain it over long periods of time.

Benday process, mistograph.—Mechanical means are available for creating various dot or line patterns on plates to give the effect of wash drawings and even to produce simple effects similar to process color. The earliest of these mechanical methods is called benday after its inventor, Ben Day. This makes use of inked screens to print patterns either on the negative or on the metal plate. Combinations of different screens in controlled areas produce many useful effects, particularly for newspaper advertising.

The artist may produce stipple or screen effects in another way. Using prepared paper, such as so-called *mistograph* sheets, a drawing is made and inked in. Then a special solution is applied with a brush to the areas where stipple effects are wanted. Wherever it is applied this solution develops out dots that are latent in the prepared paper.

Transparent sheets of thin celluloid which have been printed with screens or other patterns also are available. The artist cuts these to fit the areas that require shading and affixes them to his drawing with special adhesives.

Duplication of letterpress forms. — There are many cases in letterpress printing when it is not advisable or not feasible to print directly from the original type forms. Newspapers, for example, use curved plates. Commercial printers save expense by printing a number of duplicates at once. Magazines like the *Saturday Evening Post* can complete their enormous press runs only by having dozens of presses all printing the same pages. These are only a few of the situations which require duplication of original type pages in plate form.

For making letterpress plates, two methods are commonly used: *electrotyping* and *stereotyping*. Both produce relief plates, which may be either flat or curved.

Stereotyping.—The larger newspapers use the stereotyping process to make curved page plates for their high-speed perfecting presses. After a page is complete and locked up, it is transported on its truck to the stereotyping room. Here a *stereotype matrix*, or "mat," made of paper and plastic materials, is laid face down on the type and topped off with a felt or cork blanket. A heavy roller press then molds the mat to the page.

Two kinds of mats are in use. One is kept moist; the other is used bone-dry. The first, or *wet mat*, must be dried after molding for about fifteen minutes on a heated steam table. Heavy pressure is employed to hold the blanket and mat tightly in place while this drying operation is taking place.

The *dry mat* has been perfected comparatively recently but has supplanted the wet mat in most newspaper plants. The speed with which it is finished is, of course, tremendously important, for minutes count on any paper. More than this, dry mats make possible savings in paper that count up into large sums in the course of a year. These mats shrink heavily before casting. The greater shrinkage takes place across the page width, and affects its length in a lesser degree. This may make it possible to reduce the width of the paper rolls nearly an inch. On a few hundred thousand copies this runs into many pounds.

After a mat has been rolled and dried thoroughly, it is placed inside a cylindrical casting box which is provided with a central steel core, and molten metal is pumped into the space between the mat and the core. The resulting semicylindrical plate is withdrawn from the casting box, shaved inside, and trimmed. It is then ready to be clamped on the steel press cylinder, where it covers approximately half its circumference. A second plate completes the circle, allowing marginal space between heads and tails of the plates.

Stereotype mats do not have to be used immediately, nor are they fragile. Practically all comic strips and news features are received by newspapers in mat form. Mats are also supplied by special services for illustrating advertisements. A large percentage of the national advertisers supply newspapers with stereotype mats of their advertisements.

Flat casts from mats so received by a newspaper sometimes are made to type height; or, more frequently, they are cast as thin plates which are laid on metal bases in the newspaper forms. For printing on flat-bed presses either thin casts mounted on wood blocks or type-high casts are used. *Stereotypes* may include half-tones, line etchings, type matter, or combinations of these. Whatever appeared in the original type-high forms from which mats are rolled will be reproduced with reasonable fidelity in the newspaper-page plates.

Stereotype plates formerly were used for book pages, which are plated to reduce costs in quantity production and to avoid the keeping of type pages in storage. Most book work is printed now, however, from electrotype plates.

Electrotyping.—When high fidelity to the originals is required, *electrotypes,* which are much harder than stereotypes, are used. Carefully made electrotype plates will produce printed impressions which are indistinguishable from the impressions of the original type and illustrations.

Pages to be electrotyped are locked up carefully, and then they are molded in a sheet of mineral wax of about the consistency of hard paraffine. This wax mold, called a *case,* is coated with finely powdered graphite, and then is immersed in an electroplating bath. By means of an electric current a thin sheet of copper is deposited upon the surface of the mold, which exactly duplicates the surface of the original type form.

When the coating of copper is thick enough, the mold is removed from the bath, the wax is melted off, and the copper "shell" is backed up with lead.

Most electrotypes are made by depositing copper on the mold. However, nickel and chromium also are used. Very often plates are started in a nickel bath and then finished up in a copper bath. This method produces a thin printing surface of nickel on a copper shell. Such plates are known in the trade as *steel-faced electrotypes.* They wear longer than copper-faced plates, and also are unaffected by the chemical action of certain inks. (Copper darkens many red inks, and some blue inks etch this metal away.)

For making electrotypes of four-color-process half-tones, sheet lead is used to make the molds instead of wax. Plates made in this way are not only absolutely faithful in detail but free from distortions which occur in wax molds, which may easily stretch or shrink. The lead-molded plates register when printed exactly as the originals do. Only unmounted copper or zinc half-tones can be molded in lead; type matter or wood-base cuts would be crushed by the great pressure used in this process.

A material for molding either type forms or plates which is free from the faults of wax, yet soft enough to yield satisfactory molds under moderate pressures, is now widely used. It is known as *tenaplate,* and is a combination of metal and resilient materials.

Rubber printing plates.—Rubber stamps have been manufactured for office uses since Civil War days. These usually are vulcanized on plaster of paris molds made from printers' types. Rubber plates also have long been used for printing on tin, on wooden boards, or on burlap bags. These plates formerly were cut by hand from sheet rubber. Within the present decade, however, precision presses have been developed for making plates by direct molding of type forms or of photoengraved plates. The molds are a form of phenolic resin, similar to bakelite. Raw rubber is vulcanized on these molds to make rubber plates for use in either flat-bed or rotary letterpress printing. The molding and vulcanizing equipment for making rubber plates has been developed and marketed as a means whereby the letterpress printer may produce his own duplicate plates at a low cost.

Half-tones in molded rubber form may be printed on uncoated papers with fairly satisfactory results.

CHAPTER TEN

Paper and Ink

**Materials used in manufacture of paper; the paper
trade and its customs; specifying paper; classes of
papers; testing papers; printing inks**

PAPER was invented by the Chinese about A.D. 100 and was
introduced into Europe in the twelfth century. Paper is of fundamental importance to so many processes and is used for so many
purposes that its part in modern civilization is a major one.

Cellulose, obtained in the form of fibers from plants and
trees, is one of nature's most indestructible substances. These
fibers are unaffected by most chemicals and in their pure form
do not deteriorate with age and are not affected by exposure to
sunlight or moisture.

Fibers from plants.—Until the middle of the last century,
linen and cotton fibers derived from rags were practically the
only materials used in making paper. Books and manuscripts
on rag-fiber papers four or five hundred years old are still in
an excellent state of preservation. At present, only a limited
amount of all-rag sheets are manufactured, but rag fibers are
added to sulphite pulp for producing writing and book papers
of varying degrees of permanence.

Fibers from trees.—Constantly increasing demands for
paper led experimenters to seek new sources of cellulose fibers.
In 1865 fibers obtained by cooking wood with sodium sulphite

144

came into general use, and today over 95 per cent of our paper is derived from forest products.

Various woods are utilized, spruce, hemlock, and poplar being leaders in volume. Paper mills are necessarily located near available forest areas, and require also an abundance of clear, pure water. For this reason most mills are to be found in the northern states or in Canada.

The inroads on standing forests have been a cause of concern to papermakers and others, particularly on account of the enormous daily consumption of paper for newspapers, which deforests hundreds of acres every day. Recently a method has been devised for using quick-growing Southern pine wood, with the prospect of re-forestation at a rate that will provide adequately for future newspaper consumption.

Mechanical production of fibers.—Newsprint is made up principally of fibers obtained by grinding up logs on grindstones with a great amount of water. The resulting product is called *groundwood pulp*, or mechanical wood pulp.

Newsprint lacks strength, and turns dark upon exposure to light. In a year or so it becomes brittle and disintegrates. The cause of this impermanence of newsprint is the drying effect of the foreign substances, notably resins and lignin, with which the cellulose fibers are mixed. Mechanical pulp, therefore, is used only for the cheapest papers, where permanence is not a factor.

Chemically treated wood.—Wood chips cooked under pressure in a solution of sodium sulphite or other acid salt break up into cellulose fibers and soluble substances. After eight to twenty hours of cooking, the cooked product is washed with water to remove the foreign substances.

Next the fibers are bleached, if white paper is to be made. If now the bleaching agents are completely washed out, the resulting fibers are relatively permanent.

Comparison of fibers.—Cellulose fibers are minute tubes. They may be seen along the edges of torn paper. Those from linen or cotton may be as long as an inch or more; wood fibers average less than one-eighth of an inch in length.

Linen and cotton fibers are derived from old rags and from scraps of new fabrics obtained as by-products of various manufacturing operations. These fibers are notable for their strength and pliability. Their cost is, of course, prohibitive for most purposes.

Wood fibers are relatively cheap and plentiful, and while they are not so strong as linen or cotton they may be processed in ways that make them tough and pliable. In general, papers made from wood fibers are deficient in strength, although they are more opaque, and more even in texture, than papers made wholly or partly of rags.

Paper machines.—Paper formerly was made by hand. Over one hundred years ago a machine was devised for the purpose, and these *Fourdrinier* machines are universally used today. The average machine costs upward of a quarter of a million dollars. Very large machines used for making newsprint in great quantities cost several millions.

In operation, the cellulose fibers, in 98 or 99 times their volume of water, flow onto a moving wire screen. The water drains through the screen, and the web of felted fibers transfers to an endless felt blanket, on which it passes between a series of heated rollers. Leaving the blanket, the web of paper continues on through other heated rollers which finish the drying process.

Some idea of the magnitude of these machines may be had from the fact that one news mill in Oregon produces a web of paper 20 feet wide at the rate of 15 miles an hour, or at the rate of 110 tons of finished paper a day.

Finishing processes.—Various finishes are imparted to papers in the making. For example, clay and an adhesive sizing may be added to the fibers before they flow onto the wire screen. The resulting paper will be quite smooth and very opaque. Such papers are used for printed books and magazines.

Papers intended for writing purposes are sized in the paper-making machine, or are dipped into a tub of sizing after leaving the paper machine. For this purpose animal glues are used. The sizing used in book papers is made from resins and alum.

Very smooth *coated* papers are actually painted on one or both sides with a sort of kalsomine made of casein and white pigments. High polish is given such sheets by the process known as *calendering*, in which the paper is passed between heavy polishing rolls.

The wire screens used in paper machines are very fine in texture and do not noticeably mark the sheet. This paper is described as *wove*. However, some papers are made which show a distinct wire-pattern when held to the light. These are the so-called *laid* papers. Watermarks, which appear in most writing papers to identify the brands, are impressed in the wet paper by a *dandy roll*.

Handmade papers are distinguished for having irregular, thinner edges, called *deckle edges*. In machine-made papers some fibers creep under the *deckle straps* at the sides of the machine, giving a *deckle edge* to the paper, which is often retained in better grades of book papers in imitation of handmade sheets.

Divisions of paper merchandising.—Papers used for writing and printing are classed as *fine* papers. Those used for wrapping and packaging are called *coarse* papers. Besides these two classes there are numerous paper products which because of the limited nature of their uses are called *specialties*.

Manufacture and sale of papers usually divides sharply along these lines.

A paper for every purpose.—The variety and range of physical properties in paper is tremendous. In relative strength, for example, the range is from cigarette paper to cover papers so strong that they resist any effort to tear them. In color, papers can be had in the full range of the spectrum and in all modulations and modifications. And so on. There is indeed a paper for every purpose to which this material conceivably can be applied.

In describing a paper, it may be necessary to state some or all of the following physical characteristics: Kind of paper, size, weight, color, texture, finish, grain (direction of fibers), and, in the case of cardboards, method of manufacture.

Classification of papers.—There are at least six groups of papers in common use for writing and printing purposes. These differ from one another in their physical characteristics.

Writing papers.—This group includes bonds, ledgers, thin papers, mimeographs, flat writings, and safety papers, all of which are made specifically for writing purposes.

The basic size in which writing papers are stocked and sold is 17 x 22 inches. Thicknesses of all papers are stated in terms of their weight, since it is impracticable to measure paper thickness directly. Although it is the custom to refer to the weight of a ream (500 sheets) of the standard or basic size of the kind of paper involved, paper is ordered and its cost calculated on the basis of weight per thousand sheets. Writing papers, in size 17 x 22, range from 7 pounds to 36 pounds to the ream. In other words, the thickest is more than five times as thick as the thinnest.

Bond papers receive pen-and-ink writing readily; they are usually tough and strong; they crackle when handled; and they are relatively transparent. Bonds range in quality from cheap "sulphite" sheets, which are little better than newsprint, up to fine all-new-rag papers. Bonds are made in a wide range of colors and finishes. The grades which are used for most business correspondence are made of high-grade, pure, clean wood fibers, sometimes with a small admixture of cotton-rag fibers.

Customary sizes for bonds are 17 x 22, 19 x 24, and 17 x 28 inches, and, inasmuch as these sizes are cut from rolls, sheets double the basic size—that is, 22 x 34—and doubles of the other sizes named, are readily obtainable.

Ledger papers are heavy, strong bond papers, having the same basic size, and of weights from 24 to 36 pounds per ream. As the name implies, they are used primarily for business records. Most ledgers contain a percentage of rag fibers for permanence.

Book papers.—These seldom are very strong, but necessarily are opaque for two-side printing. In finish they range from blotter-like *eggshell books* through various degrees of smoothness up to glass-smooth coated sheets. It is desirable that book papers fold without cracking and that they absorb printing ink readily.

The colors and textures of book papers cover a wide range, with many decorative characteristics intended to give novelty and eye-appeal to advertising matter.

The basic size for book papers is 25 x 38 inches. Weights per ream of 500 sheets range from 20-pound "Bible paper" up to 150-pound. Sheets thicker than this usually are classed as cover papers.

Other customary sizes for book papers are $22\frac{1}{2}$ x 35, 28 x 42, 32 x 44, and "doubles" of these and of the standard 25 x 38 size.

Newsprint.—This is a weak and impermanent sheet, irregular in texture and mottled in color. The basic size for sheet news is 24 x 36 inches. Reams of this size weigh 32, 36, or 40 pounds. Perfecting presses, either flat-bed or rotary, use newspaper in rolls of various widths.

Cover papers.—As the name implies, these papers are used as covers for books, pamphlets, magazines, and for containers of various kinds. The number and variety of cover papers are too great for any brief characterization. In general, they are relatively stronger than book papers, are resistant to wear and abrasion, are usually decorative in some fashion, and are available in many of the stronger and brighter colors.

The basic size for cover paper is 20 x 26 inches; a second

common size is 23 x 35. Weights range from 35 pounds per ream
in box covers, to as much as 480 pounds. The most common
weights are 50, 65, and 80 pounds per ream, and "double thick."

Cardboards.—Some boards are made by pasting together
two or more thinner sheets. These are called *pasted bristols.*
Other boards are made by assembling several thicknesses of
wet pulp in a special type of paper-making machine. These are
called *millboards.*

The standard size for bristols and other cardboards intended
for printing purposes is 22½ x 28½ inches. Artist's boards
and boards used in boxmaking are made in other, larger sizes.
These boards usually are packaged and sold in 100-sheet lots.

Thickness of cardboards and millboards is specified in
various ways. Some are described by the weight of 500 sheets.
Others are said to be 2-ply, 3-ply, 4-ply, and so on up to 12-ply
or more, according to the number of sheets which are pasted together in making them. The heavy, coarse millboards usually
are specified by giving their thickness in *points,* that is, in thousandths of an inch. A 25-point board, for example, will average
25/1000 of an inch in thickness.

Index bristols are very heavy grades of ledger papers,
and are used for record cards of various kinds and sizes. These
sheets are suitable for pen-and-ink writing or for typing purposes; they erase well, and—most important of all—they are
stiff enough to stand up in card file boxes. Grain (see below) is
highly important in index cards. It must run vertically in any
card which stands on edge.

Index bristols are packaged and sold in 100-sheet lots.
Weights, however, are stated in terms of 500 sheets. The basic
size in most parts of the United States is 25½ x 30½ inches. In
some of the Atlantic states the customary size is 20½ x 24¾
inches.

Specialties.—This group includes gummed papers, metallic
papers, decorators' papers, etc.

Grain in paper.—In flowing onto the wire screen of the paper machine the fibers tend to arange themselves parallel to the direction of flow. This imparts to all machine-made papers a well-defined *grain*, similar in many ways to the grain in wood.

Papers fold more easily along the direction of the grain. Folding across the grain tends to crack the sheet. In bound books the grain of the paper always should parallel the binding. As has been noted, cards which are to stand on edge should be cut from the sheet with the grain vertical.

Paper tests.—There are various ways of measuring the strength of papers. One machine, called a Mullen Tester, forces a small rubber ball through the sheet and measures the pressure required to do this. Another machine folds an inch-strip back and forth until it breaks.

Direction of the grain usually can be determined by folding the sheet. In case of doubt, a small piece, marked in some way to show how it has been taken from a large sheet, may be floated on water for an instant. The expansion of the fibers of the wetted side of the sample will curl it in a direction parallel to the grain. This indication then can be referred to the larger sheet.

Pasted boards can be distinguished from millboards by setting fire to a small strip. The "plies" of the pasted boards separate as the burning proceeds.

Formula for calculating the cost of paper.—Multiply the weight of a ream by two, to get the weight of 1,000 sheets. Multiply this result by the number of sheets required to obtain the total weight in pounds. Then multiply again by the price per pound expressed in cents, and point off five places in the final result.

Example: How much will 875 sheets of 17 x 22 bond cost, if a ream of the paper weighs 16 pounds, and the price per pound is 15 cents?

16 (pounds per ream) $\times$ 2 = 32 (weight of 1,000 sheets)
32 $\times$ 875 = 28,000 $\times$ 15 cents = 420,000
Point off five places . . . . $4.20 answer

Printing inks.—In their composition most printing inks are simply well-made, heavy-bodied paints. Like ordinary house paints, their principal constituents are three in number: pigments, vehicles, and drying agents. These may be classified as follows:

Pigments
   1. Inorganic
      a) Earth colors: example, burnt sienna
      b) Metallic oxides: example, cover white (titanium dioxide)
      c) Chemical compounds: example, ultramarine blue (potassium ferro-ferri cyanide)
   2. Organic
      a) Synthetic dyes: example, monastral blue
      b) Natural substances: example, lampblack

Vehicles
   1. Inorganic
      a) Hydrocarbons: example, paraffine oil
      b) Ethers
   2. Organic
      a) Linseed oil
      b) Tung oil
      c) Cottonseed oil
      d) Other vegetable products

Dryers
   1. Inorganic
      a) Manganese compounds
      b) Cobalt compounds
      c) Other metallic oxidizing agents
   2. Organic
      a) Natural resins: example, copal
      b) Varnishes made from linseed oil
      c) Synthetic resins

With so wide a selection of materials it is possible to make inks for almost any purpose, in any color or shade of color, and with many and varied other physical characteristics.

Prices of inks vary extremely, and depend upon (1) cost of ingredients and (2) the care with which the inks are compounded. Inks used for commercial printing and lithographing range in price from a few cents to several dollars a pound. Colored inks relatively cost more than blacks. An average price for inks used in commercial printing would be about 50 cents per pound.

News inks.—The black inks used for newspaper printing necessarily are very inexpensive as compared with other inks. News inks are compounded to flow freely and to dry quickly, principally by absorption into the paper of the vehicles used. Presses which "perfect" the sheet by printing it on both sides in a continuous operation require special blankets for the purpose of preventing offset or smutting.

Several new types of inks which dry almost instantaneously have been introduced recently. One variety, now widely used in commercial printing, "sets" instantly when the printed sheets are passed over a gas flame.

Another new ink is solid at ordinary temperatures, and has the appearance of lumps of coal. This ink is used on presses in which the ink and all parts of the press which are used in applying it to the paper are heated to 200 degrees Fahrenheit. When the heated ink, which flows freely at this temperature, reaches the cold surfaces of the paper, it re-solidifies instantly.

Still another new ink is so constituted that it dries immediately upon exposure to water vapor. Presses which use this ink, as well as those which use the solid kind just described, must be equipped especially for their use. This has prevented newspapers from making experiments with them. Ultimately, however, they may be used in the production of the larger dailies.

Selected Bibliography

HISTORY OF PRINTING

The Book: the Story of Printing and Bookmaking, by DOUGLAS C. MC-
MURTRIE. Covici-Friede, New York. 1937.

A readable, compact account of the art from the days of Gutenberg to the present time.

Printers and Printing, by DAVID POTTINGER. Harvard University Press.
1941.

PRINTING INDUSTRY

The Building of a Book, ed. by FREDERICK H. HITCHCOCK. R. R. Bowker, New York. 1929.

Information on printers' rollers, printing inks, photoengraving, intaglio processes, lithography, and bookbinding.

The Printing Trades and Their Workers, by FLORENCE E. CLARK. International Textbook Co., Scranton, Pa. (1939)

Each of the various printing crafts or occupations is described in this book, and the demand for workers is analyzed.

TYPE FACES

Printing Types: Their History, Forms, and Use, by DANIEL BERKELEY
UPDIKE. Harvard University Press, Cambridge, Mass. 1937.

A scholarly account of the development of type designs in various countries, with many examples.

Production Yearbook. Published annually by Colton Press, New York.

This annual omnibus of printing knowledge and the development of the industry during the year always features a section in which every type face which has appeared anywhere during the year is shown in a one-line specimen.

Typographer's Desk Manual, by EUGENE DE LOPATECKI. Ronald Press,
New York. (1937)

This book shows 29 type faces which are in common use and points out their identifying characteristics. Copy-fitting is explained in detail, and the uses of the various types are explained.

TYPOGRAPHY IN GENERAL

The Practice of Typography, by THEODORE L. DEVINNE. Century Co.,
New York. 1902.

The standard treatise on printing style and typographical niceties.

Printing for School and Shop, by FRANK S. HENRY. John Wiley & Sons, New York. (1917)

Of the many school textbooks, this is the most complete and authoritative.

General Printing, by CLEETON AND PITKIN. MacKnight & MacKnight, Bloomington, Ill. (1941)

This complete laboratory manual for the operations of typesetting and press-work, shows by photographs the details of every step.

Instruction Sheets in an Elementary Course in Printing, by HARTLEY E. JACKSON. San Jose State College (mimeographed). 1941.

NEWSPAPER TYPOGRAPHY

Newspaper Makeup, by JOHN E. ALLEN. Harper & Bros., New York. 1936.

The Modern Newspaper, by JOHN E. ALLEN. Harper & Bros., New York. 1940.

The profuse examples in these two books cover practically every phase of news-paper headlines and page make-up.

Editing the Day's News, by BASTIAN AND CASE. The Macmillan Company, New York. 1932.

A chapter on headlines contains much practical advice.

PAPER AND PAPERMAKING

Printing Papers, by W. E. WHEELWRIGHT. University of Chicago Press. 1936.

A thoroughly practical discussion of the printing qualities of various papers is a feature of this book.

Manufacture of Pulp and Paper, by JOINT EXECUTIVE COMMITTEE of the vocational education committees of the pulp and paper industry of the United States. McGraw-Hill & Co., New York (n.d.).

This is an exhaustive, five-volume work that covers in technical fashion all phases of the industry.

PROOFREADING

Proofreading and Copy-Preparation, by JOSEPH LASKY. Mentor Press, New York. 1941.

In the 656 pages of this book is contained a tremendous store of information upon every subject that comes within the field of proofreading. The training of proofreaders and of copyholders is discussed, and the practical operations of a proofroom are described.

A Manual of Style. University of Chicago Press. 1937.

The tenth edition of this authoritative work brings up to date the wealth of useful information it contains. There is much to be gained by any person from even a simple reading of this book.

Glossary

Composing Room and General Printing Terms

agate—type which sets 14 lines to the inch; a common measure of advertising space.

alignment—accurate relationship of adjacent letters to an even base line on a horizontal plane.

alterations—changes from original copy made by author.

ascenders—vertical, upward-reaching portions of type faces.

bank, bank man—table where machine-set type is received from operator, and man who assembles such type.

bastard—printers' adjective, descriptive of any irregular piece of material, and by extension, term for all irregularities.

battery—same as **bank.**

black letter—the Gothic, or Old English letter, used in the earliest books, and still used in Germanic countries.

bleed—*see* Engraving Terms.

body type—textual matter, as distinguished from headings or display lines.

bold-face—versions of type designs in which the letter strokes are thickened.

box heading—headline enclosed in a ruled-line "box."

brayer—inking roller for hand use.

brevier—archaic name for a certain size of type, approximately 8-point.

cabinet—article of composing-room furniture, usually a container for type cases; a name applied to any holder of drawers, cases, or furniture.

caption—an identifying title above an illustration. See **legend.**

case—tray for holding types, divided into boxes according to various schemes; **news cases**—double cases used in setting large quantities of type by hand (*cap case*—upper case; *lower case*—container for minuscule or lower-case letters); **California job case**—standard form of case, containing boxes for all usual capital and lower-case characters.

chase—steel or cast-iron frame in which type forms are assembled and locked up for the press.

composing rule—brass or steel rule used in stick to separate line which is being assembled from those which have been completed.

copy—any written, typewritten, drawn, painted, or photographed material which is to be reproduced in print.

copy-cutter—contact man between editorial room and the composing room and supervisor of mechanical and factual features of copy passing through his hands.

cut-in sidehead—subheading, usually in a distinctive type face, which is set into the opening lines of a paragraph in a space allowed for the purpose.

cut-off rules—full-width rules which are used in newspapers to separate editorial matter from advertisements, or to separate type from illustrations, or to separate advertisements from each other.

dashes—short rules used between stories or to separate the elements of headlines.

dead—term for used or discarded copy, type, or other material; **dead bank**—table or stone on which dead type and cuts are stored preliminary to being returned to cases or remelted.

deck—any secondary element of newspaper heading.

descenders—portions of letters *g, j, p, q,* and *y* which descend below the lower line of other letters.

dirty proof—proofsheet full of errors.

display—(*noun*) large-type lines in advertisements; (*verb*) to set words or lines in a way that will give them prominence.

distribution—process of putting type back in case; any "putting away" process.

double-leaded—wide spacing between lines; sometimes used in type matter to give emphasis.

dump—same as **bank.**

Élite—small typewriter type, which measures 12 characters to the inch.

em—square unit corresponding to any type size; **set em**—em measured linewise, that is, horizontally. The em is often called a "mutton" or "mut" to distinguish it from an *en.*

en—half an *em;* often called a "nut."

family—as applied to type, a number of faces which derive from a common parent design.

fitting—the interrelationship between adjacent letters in type lines; *fitting* is good if the letters are well adjusted to each other in every combination; **close fitting**—minimum spacing between adjacent letters.

font—a full assortment of type of one size and style.

foot slug—blank slug at bottom of type column.

form—a chase filled with relief printing materials, and locked up ready for press.

form truck—iron-topped rolling table on which newspaper pages are assembled.

frame—top of cabinet or case rack upon which compositor works.

fudge mold—Linotype mold for casting tapered slugs; **fudge plate**—special receptacle in press cylinder to receive tapered slugs bearing baseball scores or last-minute news.

furniture—metal or wooden strips used to surround type matter in chase and to assist in lockup; any large pieces of blanking-out material.

galley—brass or steel tray, with rim around three sides, used to contain type matter while it is being set or worked on.

galley proof—preliminary proof of type matter as it appears before paging.

hanging indention—runover set back from the flush-left beginning in style like this Glossary.

hellbox—the limbo into which worn and broken type and other discarded printing material descends.

initial—large letter used at beginning of paragraph.

ink knife—spatula used for handling and mixing printers' ink.

Intertype—slug-composing machine, manufactured in competition with the Mergenthaler Linotype.

italic—sloping versions of Roman type faces. Sloping Sans Serifs are more correctly described as "oblique" designs.

justify—to make even; to space out evenly; to tighten in any way.

keep standing—direction given when type matter is to be held for possible future use.

kerned letters—types having projections which overhang adjacent letters.

keyboard—arrangement of keys by which type is mechanically composed; also the Monotype machine unit which punches tape for operating the caster.

kill—direction to throw away type matter that has been printed or is not to be used.

layout—(*noun*) diagram or other indicated plan for the arranging of pages or other type forms; **lay out** (*verb*) to plan pages, advertisements, or other type arrangements.

lead cutter—bench shear device for cutting leads to accurate lengths.

leads, leading—(*noun*) strips of lead (or brass) used to insert between lines of type; usually 2 points thick; (*verb*) **lead out**—to space out by putting leads between lines.

legend—descriptive words or lines used under an illustration.

letterpress—any printing process which makes use of raised, or relief, surfaces.

ligatures, logotypes—ligatures are combinations of two or more connecting letters on one body; logotypes are combinations of two or more *separate* letters as one type.

linage—measure of advertising space, usually the total space used or to be used in a given time, expressed almost invariably in agate lines.

line—(*verb*) to align; alignment; (*noun*) measure of wood type, equal to one pica. A 5-line wood type is five picas high.

line-gauge—wooden or brass ruler graduated in picas and/or agate lines. A compositor uses a line-gauge continually.

Linotype—the original line-composing machine. By means of a manually operated keyboard, it assembles matrices from which it casts solid lines of type, and finally returns the matrices to their original places in the magazine.

live matter—type matter which is to be used, as contrasted with dead matter, which is to be thrown away.

lockup—the securing of type and other material in a form or chase, using quoins or other mechanical devices for exerting pressure against sides.

lower case—small or minuscule letters, as distinguished from capitals, or uncials.

magazine—container for matrices on Linotype or Intertype machines, from which they are withdrawn through the action of keyboard keys and an escapement mechanism.

make up—(*verb*) to assemble type matter and other printing materials in pages or other organized forms.

make-up rule—steel rule, often called "hump-backed rule," used for handling type into form, and for innumerable other purposes.

matrix—brass die in which is impressed the imprint of a type letter or letters. Matrices are used for casting separate types for the case, or other forms of matrices are assembled in lines, from which solid lines of type are cast.

matrix case—holder for a set of Monotype composition matrices.

measure—width of type line, generally expressed in picas or half-picas.

minuscule—small or lower-case letters, as opposed to *majuscules,* or capitals.

mixer—line-composing machine which assembles and automatically distributes matrices from two or more separate magazines.

mold—steel cell, usually adjustable, in which are cast separate types or whole lines, as the case may be; **mold wheel, mold disk**—gear-driven, rotating carrier for Linotype or Intertype molds.

Monotype—a machine which casts and assembles justified lines of separate types, or which makes single types, rules, and spacing materials. For composition the Monotype uses two separate devices, a keyboard and a caster.

mortise—*see* Engraving Terms.

nonpareil—old name for type, approximately 6-point; a common name for a 6-point slug, or for a measure of 6 points.

phat—any type and/or material that is kept back from distribution upon the chance that all or a part of it may be used again.

pi—type or other material which has fallen down in disorder; hence (*verb*) to disarrange type through incautious handling, or, by extension, to disorganize anything.

pica—standard unit of printers' measurement, very nearly one-sixth of an inch; **pica em**—unit one pica square; **pica type**—former name for 12-point.

point—fundamental unit of printers' measurements. A point is almost exactly one seventy-second of an inch.

pot—container for molten metal used in typecasting machines.

proof—any trial impression of type or printing material.

proof planer—wooden block covered with felt, used for making hand proofs.

proof press—simple press for pulling proofs.

quads—abbreviation for quadrats, which are type-spacing elements one em or larger in size.

quoins—sliding wedges or spring locks used to apply lateral pressure to type forms in locking up; **quoin key**—wrench of special design used to operate quoins.

reglets—wooden strips, usually pica or half-pica, used in place of metal slugs, or alongside quoins in locking up.

relief—printing processes or materials are termed *relief* when the surfaces which receive ink are raised above the non-printing areas.

revise—(*noun*) trial proof pulled to show that corrections marked in a previous proof have been correctly made; (*verb*) any of the processes for checking the accuracy with which type corrections previously marked have been made.

roman—the most familiar form of type letter, having pronounced *serifs*, or terminal elements, and usually exhibiting a noticeable contrast between the various strokes which make up letter forms.

rules—metal or brass type-high strips, used for printing continuous lines.

run in—to set continuously, without paragraphs.

script—type forms which resemble handwriting, notably the historical "Secretary" hands. Scripts are joined forms; *Cursives* resemble scripts, but the individual letters are not joined to each other.

serifs—terminal portions of letter strokes.

set—a term specifying the closeness or wideness of the fitting of letters; frequently heard in connection with Monotype composition in which the set is variable at will.

set solid—to compose type without space between lines.

shoulder—blank space at bottom of type face, to accommodate descending strokes.

sidehead—title which appears at the left margin of a page; also heads which appear in the margins. *See* cut-in sidehead.

signature—store nameplate or name slug; one binding section of a book.

slug—(*noun*) a blank spacing strip of 6 points or more in thickness; the type product of a line-composing machine; (*verb*) to space out widely between lines; (*proofreading*) to read only the first or last word of each (slug) line, as a quick method of checking possible displacement of lines in machine-set matter.

slug line—numbered identification line at top of a galley to keep continuity of matter set.

spaces—blank type elements of various widths used between words.

standing matter—type set up and held in reserve.

starter—the final page or plate of a newspaper edition.

stick—short for composing stick, used in setting type by hand; pan or tray which receives the slugs from slug-composing machine.

straight matter—body type or text matter.

style—printing style includes innumerable niceties of indention, spelling, punctuation, capitalization, and other usage, which should be uniform in a newspaper, or in the product of a commercial plant; **style book**—a compilation in book form of all elements of good usage and office style.

swash letters—decorative italic capitals, used as alternative characters with regular capitals.

tabular matter—type composition consisting of figures (or letters) in columns, with or without vertical rules.

take—portion of copy "taken" from copy hook at one time.

take-slug—numbered slug placed at the head of composed matter to identify product of individual workman.

thirty—"that's all"; universal symbol (30) and phrase of completion of day or task.

turtle—form truck.

upper case—term infrequently used to denote capital letters or the case in which they are kept.

wrong font—letter from one font of type which appears by mistake in matter set in another font.

Pressroom Terms

back up—to print the reverse side of a sheet which already has been printed on one side.

bed—part of a platen or a cylinder press upon which the type-form is supported.

bleed—*see* Engraving Terms.

copperplate printing—much "society" printing, that is, visiting cards and social announcements, is produced from hand-engraved copper plates. This is the most common form of intaglio printing.

cylinder press—any letterpress machine which employs a cylinder and flat-bed action.

flat-bed press—a term loosely applied to any cylinder letterpress on which the type form is mounted on the bed of the press; it can also mean a platen press.

fountain—container on a press for the supply of ink, from which the ink is dispensed in accurate quantities to replace the ink used in printing.

letterpress—*see* Composing Room Terms.

make-ready—process of preparing a press so that a proper impression may be obtained from the form, usually employing hand-cut or mechanical overlays on the cylinder or platen to correct the discrepancies in type-height of type and printing plates.

mechanical overlays—a term used to describe various methods of half-tone make-ready using powdered resins, plastic materials, chalk-coated boards, or metal plates. *See* **zinc overlays.**

offset—smudging from one sheet to another, caused by excessive inking or careless handling of sheets. Such offsetting is considered a serious blemish, and printing plants employ various means to prevent it. Also a process of lithographic printing on a press employing a rubber-blanketed cylinder for the transfer of the image from plate to paper.

open, open press—said of a press that it is through with one piece of work and ready for another. One hears it said that "we shall have a press open tomorrow." Also, an *open press* is one without a mechanical feeding device.

patent bed—metal base used on press to support and secure in place standard "unmounted" electrotype plates.

perfecting press—one that prints both sides of the sheet in a continuous process.

platen press—"clam-shell" type of letterpress machine.

register—to bring into exact position. This term is used in many ways. Pages which back up—that is, which print exactly one behind another on opposite sides of the sheet—are said to be "in register."

Color plates are in register when each color is exactly in place as regards the others.

rotary press (sometimes called a "web press")—specifically a letterpress machine which employs curved printing plates. Most rotary presses print on paper from rolls, which passes through the machines in continuous webs; hence the name "web press." Lithographic presses are rotary in action, but are not classed as rotary presses.

scoring—process of creasing or excoriating a line on paper to facilitate folding.

slip-sheeting—the placing of blank sheets of paper between each pair of printed sheets as they are delivered from the press, to prevent offsetting, or to retard drying.

slitting—cutting a sheet into two or more strips as it is being delivered from a cylinder press or rotary press, by means of rotary cutting wheels through which the sheet is driven by the rotation of the cylinder.

spoilage—allowance made for losses in printing due to soiled sheets, torn sheets, folder losses, etc. Spoilage usually is estimated as a percentage of the whole number of sheets to be handled, and varies according to the number of operations through which the sheets pass.

two-color press—one in which two colors are applied in a continuous operation. There are also three-color, four-color, and multi-color presses, built for special uses. Note that "color," in this connection, may mean black. A sheet printed in black and red would be a two-color printing.

two-up—type forms duplicated and run on the press two or more at a time, to save presswork.

work and turn—a term used to describe what is done to a sheet when front and back forms are printed at opposite ends of a double-size sheet, then the sheet turned over on its shorter axis, backed up, and cut in half to make two complete finished sheets. If the sheet is turned over on its longer axis, the result is called *work and tumble*.

work and whirl—to print a double-size sheet, then whirl it about its central point and print it again on the same side of the sheet from the same type form. Complicated ruled forms are often printed in this way, with horizontal rules at one end of the sheet, vertical at the other. When the sheet is worked and whirled, two complete finished pieces result.

zinc overlays—etched mechanical overlays made from thin zinc.

Engraving and Plate-Making Terms

bearers—also called guards; type-high strips which are placed on four sides of type forms which are to be electrotyped or stereotyped.

benday—a mechanical process for applying stippled or dot patterns to printing surfaces.

bleed—term applied to designs which extend to any extreme edge of a page. In platemaking it is necessary to make such bleed designs slightly over size, so that a small portion of the illustration is trimmed off in binding.

blow up—opposed in meaning to reduce; engravers use the term specifically to describe enlargements made as line engravings from printed proofs of half-tones.

boiler plate—flat stereotype plates of column matter or pictorial features, used by smaller newspapers for filling up space when local news is lacking.

burnishing—method of increasing the size of half-tone dots by rubbing down their surfaces.

casting box—cast-iron cell, with adjustable sides, in which flat stereotypes are cast, using molten stereotype metal.

combination plate—line engraving integrally combined with half-tone.

cropping—reducing the area of a photograph so as to reproduce only the significant portion. **Crop marks** are lines drawn in the margins or on the reverse side of photographs to indicate the certain portions which are to be made into half-tone plates.

cut—loose term applied to all kinds of relief engravings.

dead metal—the excess portions of a metal plate, which surround the parts that contain the etched image; if half-tones or line etchings are to be electrotyped or stereotyped, dead metal is not trimmed off.

duographs, duotones, duotypes—terms variously applied to two-color half-tones, which can be made in several ways.

electrotype—duplication of engravings or reproduction of type in plate form; made by depositing metal electrolytically upon molds made by pressing the original relief surfaces into cerite wax, or into sheets of lead or metal alloys.

etching—removal of unwanted areas of engraving by means of chemical mordants or the action of an electric current.

half-tone—reproduction of the tones of a photograph by means of small dots of varying sizes created on the negative by photographing the copy through a half-tone screen. In letterpress, the finished half-tone plate is often called a "half-tone."

half-tone screen—two sheets of glass finely ruled with parallel lines, cemented together at right angles. Reflected light striking through this screen transfers the image of the copy to the negative in the form

of a dot pattern. Fineness of screen is varied with the surface of stock
to be printed, ranging from 50 lines to the inch to 200 or more lines.

high-light half-tones—specially made plates in which very small "high-
light" dots are entirely absent.

intaglio—printing from plates in which the design is cut or etched
below the surface.

key plate—term applied in color printing to the plate of any color which
contains those details which are required for placing the other colors
in accurate position.

line cut—zinc engraving reproducing black-and-white line copy only;
often called *zinco*.

lithography—process of printing from a flat surface which has been
treated in such a way that only desired areas will accept inking.

matrix (stereotyping)—wet or dry papier mâché sheet in which type
pages are impressed, and from which curved or flat printing plates
are cast.

mortise—(*noun*) portion removed from mounting block or beveled
plate so that type matter or other plates may be set close to the one
so mortised. Mortises usually are rectangular; if they are wholly
within the plate, they are called **inside mortises;** those which open
to the edge or corner of the plate are called **outside mortises.**

nickeltypes—electrotypes which have a thin wearing-surface of nickel
on the copper shell; used for long runs, or where inks may be affected by copper; sometimes called "steel-faced electrotypes."

offset process—usual type of lithographic process, using a press with
a rubber-blanketed intermediate cylinder.

patent blocks—iron, composition metal, or hardwood blocks, upon
which beveled printing plates are secured with movable clamps,
called **register hooks; a patent bed** is such a block large enough
to cover the whole bed of the press, thus eliminating the make-up
and lockup of separate blocks.

photolith—trade name for offset lithography using plates made by
photographic means.

planographic—having all its elements in one plane; as applied to printing plates, flat, not raised or sunken; usually denoting lithographic
plates.

plate—any flat or curved continuous printing surface, relief, planographic or intaglio, made of metal or other firm material; **plate up**
—to place plates on a press.

retouching—hand process used by artists to improve copy intended for
photoengraving.

rotogravure—intaglio process used principally for newspaper illustrated supplements.

routing—mechanical removal of excess metal from engraved plates.

screen—*see* **half-tone screen.**

stereotype—relief plate, flat or curved, cast in soft type metal from a papier mâché matrix.

tooling—any hand-engraving with a sharp tool, or graver, such as is used in half-tone work to remove dots or reduce their size.

type-high—height of printers' type, 0.918 inch.

unmounted—a specification for plates which are not to be blocked or backed up.

woodcut—hand-engraved relief printing surface cut on hard or soft wood.

zinco—line illustration photoengraved on zinc.

Paper Terms

all-rag—made entirely of fibers derived from rags.

amalgamations—permitted combinations of different grades to secure quantity price.

antique finish—surface character of book papers as they come from the papermaking machine.

bond papers—writing papers of light to medium substance, hard sized, and with a finish suitable for writing with pen or typewriter.

book papers—classification of papers, coated and uncoated, used in printing of books, magazines, and advertising matter; often qualified to mean unsized or resin-sized papers, usually uncoated.

cabinets—papeterie sets, usually of wedding stationery.

chemical—inexpensive writing paper used for second sheets; the usual color is yellow, but it is made in white, and blue, and other tints.

coated papers—printing papers having a coating of clay or other fine material, which gives them a very smooth finish.

cockle finish—pleasingly irregular surface of certain loft-dried bond papers.

deckle edges—feathery edges, usually associated with hand-made sheets, but produced artificially in other papers.

duplex papers—sheets which are intentionally two-sided, such as coated books which are white on one side and colored on the other. *See also* **two-sided.**

eggshell finish—same as antique finish.

enameled papers—high-finish coated stocks.

English finish (E.F.)—a high machine finish, smooth in texture, but not the highest gloss possible.

flat writing papers—comparatively soft papers in many grades and qualities, differing from bond papers in having less "starchiness" and crackle.

glazed papers—label and box papers to which a mirror-like surface has been given by extra calendering.

gloss papers—another name for high-finish coated stocks.

grain—in all book papers and in covers and cardboards, grain is highly important. The fibers which make up any sheet of paper lie predominantly one way. Contraction and expansion, caused by ordinary changes in temperature or humidity, take place lengthwise of the fiber only. This causes papers to curl and wrinkle. Folding is more difficult across the grain, and unless the paper grain of books parallels the binding, they will not open flat.

handmade finish—irregular surface given to some books and covers to simulate mold-made papers.

kraft—tough wrapping paper.

label papers—various kinds of paper that are finished on one side only.

linen finish—cloth-like surface given to various papers.

linen papers—flat writing grades made from linen (flax fibers).

litho coated papers—stocks which are coated, generally on one side only, with alum-free materials.

loft-dried—papers which have been dried by hanging them up in a current of air.

mimeograph papers—unsized, porous sheets used on the machine of the same name.

newsprint—very cheap paper, composed principally of ground wood with a small admixture of chemical pulp.

onionskin—a class of thin papers.

patent coated—a term used to describe certain millboards which have been finished one or both sides with bleached materials.

pulp—wood or vegetable fibers macerated, with addition of water.

ripple finish—cloudy effect produced in paper, intentionally, by admixture of heavy fibers.

ruled goods—billheads, statements, and letterheads which have been pen ruled; carried in stock by paper merchants.

safety papers—used for bank checks. Such papers have an all-over surface design which shows plainly any mechanical or chemical erasure.

sizing—a water-resistant coating applied to paper. Blotting papers are unsized. The fibers in nearly all other papers are sealed by means of water-resistant substances. Writing papers are sealed, or sized, with animal glues. For book papers, resin size, which precipitates an insoluble form of alumina on the fiber, is used.

substance—weight of 500 sheets of the basic sheet size of any paper; the common term to denote weight.

sulphite—a wood pulp prepared by cooking with a solution of sodium sulphite; a low-grade paper made from such pulp.

supercalendered (S.C.), or sized and supercalendered (S. & S.C.)— term used to designate highly finished uncoated book papers.

text—a trade name for antique book paper.

translucent—a good grade of pasted cardboard, suitable for half-tone printing.

two-sided—said of sheets in which there is a noticeable but unintentional difference between the two sides. In making paper the wire, or lower side, is more compact than the felt, or upper side. Manufacturers generally try to minimize this difference in their finishing processes.

typewriter papers—boxed sheets, cut to $8\frac{1}{2}$ x 11 or $8\frac{1}{2}$ x 13 inches, stocked in many grades of bond paper and sold usually without being printed.

watermark—identification letters or figures imparted to papers in making. These designs are made by means of a roll which presses the wet pulp.

Index